£10·95

C000154619

MARITIME
AIR
OPERATIONS

Brassey's Air Power: Aircraft,
Weapons Systems and Technology Series

VOLUME 11

Brassey's Air Power:
Aircraft, Weapons Systems and Technology Series

General Editor: AIR VICE MARSHAL R.A. MASON, CB, CBE, MA, RAF

This new series, consisting of eleven volumes, is aimed at the international officer cadet or junior officer and is appropriate to the student, young professional and interested amateur seeking sound basic knowledge of the technology of air forces. Each volume, written by an acknowledged expert, identifies the responsibilities and technical requirements of its subject and illustrates it with British, American, Russian, major European and Third World examples drawn from recent history and current events. The series is similar in approach to the highly successful Sea Power and Land Warfare series. Each volume, excluding the first, has self-test questions and answers.

Other titles in the series include:

For full details of Brassey's titles, please contact your local Brassey's Office

MARITIME AIR OPERATIONS

Group Captain B.C. Laite, RAF

BRASSEY'S (UK)
(Member of the Maxwell Macmillan Group)
LONDON · WASHINGTON · NEW YORK

UK (Editorial]	Brassey's (UK) Ltd., 50 Fetter Lane, London EC4A 1AA, England
(Orders, all except North America)	Brassey's (UK) Ltd., Headington Hill Hall, Oxford OX3 0BW, England
USA (Editorial)	Brassey's (US) Inc., 8000 Westpark Drive, Fourth Floor, McLean, Virginia 22102, USA
(Orders, North America)	Brassey's (US) Inc., Front and Brown Streets, Riverside, New Jersey 08075, USA Tel (toll free): 800 257 5755

First edition 1991

Library of Congress Cataloging-in-Publication Data
available

British Library Cataloguing in Publication Data
available

ISBN 0-08-040705 6 Hardcover

ISBN 0-08-040706 4 Flexicover

The front cover shows an F16 *Fighting Falcon* armed with the *Penguin* Mk 3 missile. (*Raytheon*)

The title page shows a *Nimrod* MR Mk 2 Maritime Patrol Aircraft. (*British Aerospace*)

Typeset by Florencetype Ltd, Kewstoke, Avon
Printed in Great Britain by BPCC Wheatons Ltd., Exeter

Foreword

Air Marshal Sir Barry Duxbury, KCB, CBE, FRIN
Director, Society of British Aerospace Companies

Maritime air operations have a special fascination for me and I suspect for all who have been involved in them. Encompassing as they do anti-submarine, anti-shipping, air defence, flight refuelling, surveillance and rescue operations, they can be of considerable tactical complexity and almost invariably involve close co-operation and co-ordination with other forces. Certainly, they demonstrate the great flexibility and reach of air power.

In recent years we have seen a wider involvement in maritime air operations yet in many maritime airmen there remains a desire to ensure that the nature and importance of these operations is better understood. For this reason Ben Laite's book is most welcome.

He has given us a very readable, expert and factual account of all land-based fixed-wing operations. Principles and concepts are described with great clarity and most helpfully illustrated with today's equipment.

This is an important book. I commend it to all who have an interest in understanding a little publicised but vital aspect of air power.

Acknowledgements

The views expressed in this book are entirely those of the author and in no way are they an expression of any official or Ministry of Defence position or statement. In compiling the book the author has drawn heavily on publications in the open press and a full list of source material is given in the bibliography. Along the way, a great many individuals have helped with advice, direction and encouragement. In particular, I must gratefully acknowledge the assistance given by Mr Mark James, of the Trenchard Library at the RAF College, Cranwell; Miss Jane Menhinnick of the Ministry of Defence Whitehall Library; Mr Chris Hobson, of the Staff College Library, RAF Bracknell; Air Vice Marshal Tony Mason, the editor of the Brassey's series on Air Power; Mr Dick Crabtree, of Thorn EMI; Group Captain Laurie Hampson, of GEC Avionics Ltd; Mr Harry Holmes of British Aerospace, Woodford; Mr Ken Allan, of Plessey Naval Systems Ltd; Mr Cliff Barnes, of Dowty Maritime Systems Ltd; HM Coastguard at Falmouth; the staff of No. 236 OCU, RAF St Mawgan; the staff of the Department of Air Warfare, RAF College, Cranwell; Squadron Leader Peter Curry; Squadron Leader Peter Howlett; Group Captain Gerry Gerrard; Mrs Fiona Barnett, for her patient and enlightened efforts in turning written manuscripts into typed pages; and, not least, my own wife, Helen, for her unselfish sacrifice of so much time that we could have spent together.

I am most grateful for the permissions to use the illustrations in the book, and acknowledgements are given with each. Crown Copyright photographs are reproduced with the permission of the Controller of Her Britannic Majesty's Stationery Office. The following organisations have helped greatly by providing illustrations: British Aerospace (Dynamics) Ltd; The RAF Museum, Hendon; Avions Marcel Dassault-Breguet Aviation; Lockheed California Company; Dowty Maritime Systems Ltd; British Aerospace, Woodford, Ltd; GEC Avionics Ltd; Ministry of Defence; Panavia Aircraft GmbH; General Dynamics; and Raytheon.

About the Author

Group Captain Ben Colston Laite was born in Lancashire and attended the Rutherford Grammar School in Newcastle upon Tyne. In 1962 he joined the Royal Air Force and was commissioned in 1963, qualifying as a navigator in 1964. He has served as a navigator on RAF squadrons operating the Vulcan bomber, the Phantom ground attack and reconnaissance fighter and the Buccaneer overland and maritime bomber. He has completed two staff tours at HQ Strike Command and one at HQ 18 (Maritime) Group and was for $2\frac{1}{2}$ years the Director of the Department of Air Warfare at the RAF College, Cranwell. Since June 1990 he has been Station Commander at RAF St Mawgan.

Contents

List of Figures

List of Plates

List of Acronyms

ADF	Automatic Direction Finding
AEW	Airborne Early Warning
ASDIC	Allied Submarine Detection Investigation Committee
ASV	Air to Surface Vessel
ATAS	Active Towed Array System
AWACS	Airborne Warning and Control System
BARRA	Beamed Array Analysis
CAMBS	Command, Active, Multibeam Sonobuoy
CAP	Combat Air Patrol/s
CASS	Command Active Sonobuoy System
CLE	Container Land Equipment
CRT	Cathode Ray Tube
CTS	Central Tactical System
CW	Continuous Wave
DF	Direction Finding
DICASS	Directional Command Active Sonobuoy System
DIFAR	Directional Frequency Analysis and Recording
ECCM	Electronic Counter Counter Measures
ECM	Electronic Counter Measures
ESM	Electronic Support Measures
FIR	Flight Information Region
FLIR	Forward Looking Infra Red
FM	Frequency Modulated
FMICW	Frequency Modulated Interrupted Continuous Wave
GNAA	German Naval Air Arm
HE	High Explosive
HF	High Frequency
IAS	Indicated Air Speed
ICAO	International Civil Aviation Organisation
IFF	Identification Friend or Foe
LOFAR	Low Frequency Analysis and Recording
MAD	Magnetic Anomaly Detector
MFG	*Marinefliegergeschwader*
MPA	Maritime Patrol Aircraft
NAS	Naval Air Station
OTHDT	Over the Horizon Detection and Targeting

RCC	Rescue Co-ordination Centre
RF	Radio Frequency
RNLI	Royal National Lifeboat Institution
SAR	Search and Rescue
SLC	Sonobuoy Launch Containers
SOSUS	Sound Surveillance System
SRR	Search and Rescue Region
SSBN	NATO term meaning nuclear submarine armed with ballistic missiles
UHF	Ultra High Frequency
VHF	Very High Frequency
VLF	Very Low Frequency

1

The Nature of Maritime Air Operations

INTRODUCTION

Origins

When the Wright brothers first took to the air in 1903 in a land-based, fixed-wing aircraft, the dreams of centuries of inventors and designers, visionaries and science fiction writers began to be realised. In the relatively short intervening period since then, the aircraft has progressed beyond those dreams and has been developed into a highly capable, reliable workhorse in many spheres. Opening up the uncharted regions of the world, speeding the trade links between nations and making swift and regular communication across continents and oceans a commonplace achievement. In the military sphere, the aircraft has made no less a contribution and has in a multitude of ways brought the method and the science of waging war up to significant technological and scientific heights.

The delivery of highly developed weapon systems over long ranges, the ability to concentrate firepower and the flexibility with which such weapons can be applied are fundamental principles of the employment of air power. These principles have been observed, studied, developed and recorded frequently, so that the modern student of air power may gather much material in order to study his subject.

The classic roles of air power have all received much coverage in books, articles and studies, and specifically in this series.

The Roles of Air Power

Aerial reconnaissance and then the more general air support of the ground forces began in earnest in World War I and developed dramatically in World War II to achieve great importance today. Air defence was seen at its pinnacle in the Battle of Britain and is still given a high priority. Strategic bombing attracted much publicity because of its controversial use against cities in World War II, and public awareness was further developed with the birth of the bombers equipped with nuclear weapons as part of the deterrent in the fifties, sixties and early seventies. Even military air transport has earned recognition as a separate activity, not only for its consistent, reliable trooping and air delivery operations, but also for its specific successes, such as the Berlin airlift and the Ethiopian famine relief flights.

The Maritime Scene

However, details involved in the conduct of maritime air operations are not so widely known. Yet this particular role within the all-encompassing umbrella of air power is extremely significant. Maritime air operations have developed over decades of technological advances, as well as over bitter periods of heavy fighting when lessons were learnt the hard way. Such operations have carved a well-deserved place in military aviation history and a truly logical and rationally argued position among the classic uses of air power today. This book seeks to provide a basis of understanding of the use of land-based, fixed-wing aircraft in maritime air operations. It should be a useful starter for those new to the maritime world and should assist in creating a complete picture for those seeking a comprehensive awareness of all aspects of air power, albeit at a basic level.

Perhaps one of the reasons for the shortage of previous, full-scale treatments of such a picture is to be found in the blurring of responsibilities and actions between air forces and navies when it comes to maritime air operations. Certainly the classic naval approach, that the aircraft is merely an extension of a fighting ship's eyes, ears and teeth, is well-founded. However, that approach is best defended when considering carrier-borne aircraft, but this is not the place to open another debate on the attributes and shortcomings of aircraft carriers nor the reasons why some nations use purely naval air forces in their maritime operations and other nations use dedicated air force assets.

Some Caveats

Nevertheless, this is an appropriate point at which to apply limits to the scope of this book. Others will write (and have written) on the advantages of large carrier battle groups with their indigenous air power, and also of helicopter forces and their contribution to the maritime scene. These authors will also write in the atmosphere of a single-service operation, all navy. This book seeks to outline the contribution to maritime air operations of land-based, fixed-wing (almost entirely) aircraft, manned and operated by air forces. This is not necessarily intended as a contribution to the argument as to whether maritime air forces should be independent of their respective navies, but the author's view will undoubtedly become clear. While other nations may operate their forces differently as part of their navy, this book will primarily take the activities of the Royal Air Force to exemplify maritime air operations.

THE COMPONENTS OF MARITIME AIR OPERATIONS

Definition

Maritime air operations may be defined as the activities of land-based, fixed-wing aircraft in pursuit of a nation's military policy, strategy and tactics at sea. Clearly, such an all-encompassing definition must be broken down into its component parts for comprehensive study. Nevertheless, before addressing these component parts it cannot be stressed often enough that the relevance and desirability of all maritime air operations must be measured in the light of that definition. If any planners in the preparation of an operation at sea are in any doubt as to whether that operation is in pursuit of a national policy, strategy or tactics at sea, they should abandon that operation.

Anti-Submarine Warfare

For the United Kingdom, there has been only one significant change in maritime policy in recent years. As the nation is dependent on foreign trade in peacetime and on external reinforcement and supply in war, protection of shipping has occupied the highest priority position. Such a policy can be identified more closely by adding that control and protection of shipping in the Atlantic is specifically the priority. However, while such a priority dominated the thinking of the higher command staffs in the Second World War, it carried with it the obvious rider that anti-submarine warfare in the Atlantic assumed that priority because the main threat to Allied shipping was from the German U-boats. Today, while the major threat to shipping in the Atlantic remains the submarine, anti-submarine warfare must contend with the other potential targets, the submarines which carry ballistic missiles to threaten national homelands. Furthermore, in the event of an opponent's deploying submarine-launched cruise missiles, there would be a need to engage in anti-submarine warfare as part of the defence of allied territory. Finally, the threat of those submarine-launched missiles against NATO naval surface units must also be countered.

Thus an equal priority aim must be to secure sea control of forward areas, to deny a potential enemy access to those areas where he needs to be in order to fire his offensive weapons.   Anti-submarine warfare is therefore one of the principle activities in maritime air operations and the only change in British policy is that the scope of that warfare has widened to counter not only the submarine threat to shipping but also the submarine threat to land targets.

Anti-Surface Unit Warfare

Surface navies have also developed so that they possess a potentially lethal punch against other surface units either commercial or military. The confident arguments from submariners that all surface vessels are good for nothing except providing targets for submarines have so far failed to persuade navies to give up their surface fleets. Accordingly, anti-surface warfare also develops inexorably as time passes and hostilities break out and then smoulder away. The aircraft has proved itself to be a potent weapon platform when used against ships; and provided that it could survive the defences long enough to reach the ship, it could deliver a crippling blow. While arguments raged back and forth on the value of immobilising a capital ship against the loss of several aircraft and crews, the weapon designers were working hard on the anti-shipping crew's dream: a stand-off weapon. Today, most units employed in the anti-shipping role are equipped with anti-ship missiles which they can fire and forget. Such units once again occupy a realistic place in the list of effective maritime air assets.

Surveillance

One shortcoming of anti-surface unit warfare is that in the realm of targeting and targeting information for the ship attackers. Thus surveillance and intelligence gathering are of primary importance, not only in building up a big, general, surface picture but also in providing current and accurate detailed information on potential targets. Surveillance is a long-term project and yet ideally suited to land-based, fixed-wing aircraft which have the range, speed, height and sensor capabilities to cover large areas in one sortie. But it is in surveillance that one discovers the clearest example of overlapping peacetime and wartime activities. Whereas surveillance of surface shipping for hostile contacts will be vital in war, there is also a parallel activity of almost equal importance in peacetime—the patrolling of fishing areas and oil fields in the ocean. Unfortunately, neither aspect of surveillance sits tidily with the requirements of an anti-submarine warfare platform. Several nations have opted for two types of maritime patrol aircraft (MAP), one for anti-submarine warfare and long-range surveillance and one for surface surveillance inshore.

Maritime Air Defence

In the general sense, air defence is a role on its own and one of the major roles of air power. However, air defence in the maritime context is such a specialised activity that it will be included here as an individual discipline. Again, the limits between a fleet and an air force responsibility, and also between a land and a maritime responsibility are somewhat blurred. Modern carriers can provide indigenous air-defence fighters and airborne early warning (AEW) aircraft, but modern land-based aircraft with air-to-air refuelling can maintain combat air patrols (CAP) at considerable distances from base. Also aircraft patrolling a particular defensive line will engage an enemy threat whether that threat is aimed eventually at a group of ships or at a country. Possessing the right command and control framework is vital in all military operations, but it may be said that it is most vital when considering air-defence operations because of the speed of reaction required.

Air–Sea Rescue

In all of these operations and the many others which involve flight across the water, there is always the risk that aircraft and crews will ditch into the sea. The operation of an efficient, quick-reaction, air–sea rescue service is therefore a sound investment for any nation intent on preserving high morale among its aircrews. The air–sea rescue of ditched aircrew has also progressed a long way since the Second World War and the days of the open dinghy and fast rescue launch. Furthermore, land-based, fixed-wing aircraft are now more generally used as control positions to manage rescues by helicopters. Such rescues are often from ships in distress rather than ditched aircraft. The air–sea rescue helicopter is the only helicopter to feature in this book and it does so because of its unique contribution to land-based, maritime air operations.

INFLUENCES ON MARITIME AIR OPERATIONS

Having briefly listed the separate components which together comprise maritime air operations, it is worth our while considering some other factors before going into each component in greater detail.

Technological Advances

Technological advances dictate the pace at which air power develops, aided more than a little by the inventiveness and vision of some thinkers and exponents of air power. While this is true in general for air power, it is fundamental to maritime air operations. The side which can first visualise an idea as to how to improve a capability and has the practical means of converting that idea into reality is the side which then possesses an advantage or edge for a period of time. Depending on how innovative the idea was and how stringent were the efforts at protecting the solution from enemy intelligence, this period may be long or short.

Costs

Another feature playing a dominant part in this aspect of air operations is the rising cost of equipment. Budgetary constraints may prevent nations from regularly investing in new equipment, sensors or weapons. However, that does not remove the need to improve. Rather such constraints throw the onus on the user to develop his existing equipment to the limit (and beyond if possible) to ensure that he sustains an edge in capability. Thus analysis of and research into current equipments and procedures must be pursued to extract maximum benefit from current equipment. The discipline of maritime air operations, dependent as it is on technology, is among the best illustrations of this point.

Human Aspects: Training, Intelligence and Co-ordination

Acquiring the technology is but one step on the long road to creating an effective maritime air force. The crews who operate the equipment need to be properly trained, given the right experiences and, just as important, given the right ideas for their motivation. As was borne out by experience in the Second World War, maritime warfare usually involves long, routine and often tedious flights over the water. It is not on every sortie that a crew will see or even get close to a submarine. Yet they must be prepared to go on doing the hard work, the painstaking picture-building which is required for the force to be effective when the day comes. Intelligence to help begin the search for either submerged or surface targets in the right area is vitally important. And to handle the often scarce assets involved in these searches, the most effective command and control arrangements need to be implemented, practised and constantly reviewed in the light of changing circumstances.

LESSONS FROM THE SECOND WORLD WAR

As we begin to build a picture of an efficient maritime air force and its component parts, together with the factors which dictate its development, it is worth examining some of the aims, decisions, implications and events in the Second World War. Although maritime operations by land-based fixed-wing aircraft were conducted on many successful occasions before the War, the history of 1939–45 contains many useful lessons and illustrations. These provide a clear insight into how the principles of maritime air operations developed. They also give some idea of the price involved in learning some of the lessons and explain why the principles have endured to the present day. These same principles dictate the shape and conduct of maritime air operations in the 1990s.

Role Definition

It will soon become clear that due to the nature of the particular aircraft involved on the Allied side, the specific roles of maritime air operations were on occasions indistinct. For example, anti-submarine warfare aircraft deployed to protect convoys from the attentions of German U-boats could also attack the Focke Wulf *Condor* aircraft, which were encountered shadowing the Allied ships. The anti-submarine warfare aircraft might discover a lifeboat full of survivors and direct a friendly destroyer or merchantman to their rescue. If the aircraft in question was actually a flying boat, or amphibian, like a *Sunderland* or a *Catalina*, then the crew themselves could effect the rescue by alighting alongside and taking the survivors aboard. Although such blurring of the specific roles was common, the Second World War does provide illustrations of those roles, beginning with anti-submarine warfare.

Anti-Submarine Warfare

The major feature of anti-submarine warfare in the Second World War was the dependence on technology and, linked very closely to that, the see-saw motion of the placing of the advantage. As the Allies developed an advantage, so the German Navy developed a countermeasure, either to restore the balance or, better still, to draw the advantage back to them. In turn, this drove the Allies to seek yet further advantages while the Germans under Admiral Doenitz were keen to develop their own gains. Admiral Doenitz had at the beginning of the war 46 submarines available for operations. Royal Air Force Coastal Command had 10 squadrons of *Ansons*; two squadrons of *Sunderland* flying boats, four squadrons of *London* and

Stranraer flying boats; one semi-operational squadron of *Hudsons*; and a 'striking force' made up of two squadrons of the obsolescent Vickers *Vildebeest*.

The Task   Coastal Command's first task was to locate as many German Naval vessels, surface and subsurface, as possible and keep them bottled up in the North Sea. However, large proportions of the German fleet had already deployed: the *Graf Spee* and the *Deutschland*, two heavy cruisers, and most of the 46 submarines were already on war stations beyond the North Sea. By now, though, clear orders were given to the aircrews that any German unit sighted was to be attacked.

The Limitations   Sadly, this was easier said than done, for the aircraft were equipped with poor quality bombs, a restrictive bomb-release gear and no anti-submarine bomb sight. Even when a submarine was sighted and attacked from low level, where it was thought that aiming errors would be so small as to be insignificant, bombs dropped on the submarine would be more of a lethal hazard to the aircraft than the submarine because of the fusing devices. Bombs exploding on impact with the sea showered the low-flying aircraft with shrapnel and splinters. Nevertheless, the Navy had been experimenting with ASDIC (derived from the Allied Submarine Detection Investigation Committee, 1917, which had instigated work on the equipment), an underwater sound transmitter which was able to receive echoes of its own transmissions bounced off any object (such as a submarine) in its path. Thus the Navy was confident that it could at least locate submerged submarines. However, the Navy also suffered from the limitations of current air-delivered bombs: on 14 September 1939 two *Skua* dive bombers from the aircraft carrier *Ark Royal* attacked the German submarine U-30. The bombs were released and upon striking the water, the fusing devices operated. However, they then bounced back into the air before exploding and both aircraft suffered shrapnel damage and crashed into the sea. The *Ansons* of Coastal Command fared little better and self-damage from their own bombs became commonplace. The only way to avoid such damage was to stay at a reasonable height when dropping the bombs; but from there, say 3,000 feet, the crews had no means of accurately aiming the bombs.

The Submarines   Doenitz may have had cause to rejoice at such ineffective retaliation against his raids on Allied shipping, but he did have his own share of problems. The U-boats were equipped with an unreliable torpedo for pressing home their attacks. On the other hand, his U-boats were able to stay at sea for long periods and cover considerable distances. By today's standards they were submersibles rather than true submarines. In other words, the U-boats conducted most of their patrols on the surface: they deployed on the surface, they searched for their prey on the surface and they attacked on the surface. They submerged mainly to escape detection and to avoid attack and also for any other tactical reason. But certainly in the early years of the war, such submersions were of short duration.

The First Kill   The first kill of a submarine by a single Allied aircraft is credited to Squadron Leader Miles Delap, when piloting a *Blenheim* bomber of Bomber Command. On 11 March 1940, Delap spotted a German submarine near

PLATE 1.1. *Sunderland* attacking U-boat. (*RAF Museum*)

Heligoland. He dived to attack and, although he was carrying bombs which would explode immediately on impact, he pressed on down the dive until he was close enough to guarantee a hit. While he was right to persist in his dive to achieve accuracy, he did so at the expense of damage to his own aircraft from shrapnel and splinters. Nevertheless, his gamble was justified in that one and possibly two of his bombs struck the submarine. It sank in only 50 feet of water and all on board were lost.

There were other Allied successes, but Doenitz's small submarine force was still able to sink about 80,000 tons of merchant shipping each month between November 1939 and May 1940. Even so, the British assessment of the effect of such losses was that they could be contained and absorbed and there was no cause for alarm.

PLATE 1.2. Vickers *Vildebeest*. (*RAF Museum*)

The Significance of the Fall of France   After the fall of France, however, the Germans were able to use the Atlantic ports on the French coast as their submarine base. No longer need the U-boats run the gauntlet of the North Sea or, worse, the Channel, to reach the open Atlantic and the lucrative reinforcement routes. The significance was felt by Coastal Command in two distinct but overlapping ways: first, the areas requiring to be searched were hugely increased and, secondly, those areas were now all some considerable distance from home bases. The short-range aircraft could not be used as efficient guardians of the North Sea and Channel areas when their prey had moved westward.

The consequences of this shift in basing were all too apparent when the average loss of shipping tonnage rose to 240,000 tons per month between June and December 1940. Even though the Navy had very early in the war applied a lesson from the First World War and had instigated a convoy system for merchant shipping, these losses were startling and recognised as potentially crippling. On his part, Doenitz had then only 27 operational U-boats, but the vast reduction in time and distance from base to the operational area had given his boats a much higher on-task time. He was able to introduce his famous 'Wolf Pack' tactics, whereby groups of U-boats operated together to attack and sink convoys. He was also able to instruct his U-boat crews to attack on the surface at night, thus providing a better opportunity for tracking a target and firing a torpedo while reducing the risk of

PLATE 1.3. *Blenheim.* (*RAF Museum*)

being detected. A surfaced submarine would not be detected by the ASDIC operated by the Navy escorts.

The Search for Solutions   As 1940 wore on, it was clear that several failings needed to be corrected in the efforts of the maritime air forces against the submarines. The only means of detecting submarines from the air was by seeing them—visual searching was a long, laborious and monotonous occupation, but still the only option open to aircrews. Worst of all, even visual search techniques were of no use if the aircraft did not have the range or endurance to get to the U-boat operating area and stay there for long enough to be effective. Thus longer-range aircraft were needed.

Also an improvement over visual search techniques was needed to overcome the problems of searching at night and when the air-to-surface visibility was low. Radar was in its infancy but aircraft of Coastal Command were using a basic air-to-surface (ASV) radar to assist in searches. The equipment had been rushed into service and was often unreliable, but non-stop efforts by research establishments and the defence industry meant that improvements were on the way.

Furthermore, the problem of self-damage from bombs needed to be addressed. Clearly what was needed was either a bombsight accurate enough to allow bombing from a 'safe' height, or bombs which could be released at low level, to guarantee accuracy, but which would detonate in such a way as to damage the submarine and not the aircraft. Although there were no bombs which fell into this latter category there was another weapon which closely met the requirement.

The naval depth charge was specifically designed to explode under water once it had reached a predetermined depth. After some trials, a modified depth bomb was declared to be the current answer to the problem. While it still had the disadvantage of breaking up ineffectually if it hit a submarine direct, and of needing to be released from heights of less than 100 feet and at speeds of less than 115 mph, these disadvantages were considered acceptable when set against the great advantage over the earlier anti-submarine bomb. The depth charge had a hydrostatic pistol which was designed to initiate the explosion at a preset depth and was considered very reliable. Also the depth charge contained a higher proportion of explosive material than the anti-submarine bomb. Thus the depth charge was more liable to explode underwater at the right depth to damage the submarine while leaving the delivery aircraft intact.

Radar   The greatest advance in technology which was of such assistance in those days of mounting ship losses was the building of the 'magnetron', a high-power oscillator, in the development of radar at the Nuffield Research Laboratory. Through the capability of this device, radar sets could generate greater power than before and could therefore receive their radar echoes from objects at much greater ranges. This was to prove a great breakthrough in the development of radar, and the practical applications were not lost on Coastal Command. However, the war on mainland Europe was also demanding technical innovation and the fruits of the new discovery were not all directed to maritime work. Even with those elements of the new technology which were available, there remained yet another problem. The new radar sets would certainly help locate the surfaced submarines and even at night.

But pressing home an attack accurately enough for a kill required the aircraft to position itself over the submarine to drop its modified depth charges. While the radar was good at detecting submarines out at three, four or seven miles depending on the aspect, as the aircraft homed in towards the target and got down to closer ranges, the blip would disappear in sea clutter and the blank area around the point of origin. Frustratingly, an aircraft might detect a submarine at night on the surface at seven miles range on the radar; it might then turn towards the vessel and use its radar to put itself on a direct track to the submarine; but before it got within visual range of the submarine, about three-quarters of a mile, the radar blip would be unusable as an aiming point. Accordingly, there was a need for yet another aid to help in the final process of localisation for attack.

The Searchlight   After a trawl of the Command for ideas, the answer settled upon was a powerful searchlight to be fitted to the aircraft. Clearly the timing of the switch-on of such a searchlight was crucial—too early and the submarine would be given enough warning to submerge unscathed; too late and the aircrew would be looking beyond the submarine, again allowing it to escape. The searchlight underwent rapid development and trials and eventually entered service as the Leigh Light. This innovative system and the new radar together dramatically improved the effectiveness of aircraft against surfaced U-boats at night. Again by the use of ideas and technology, a lucrative targeting window for the U-boats against the convoys had been closed.

Weapons   It was also about this time that the Operational Research Branch was formed at Coastal Command, and one of its first activities was an examination of all the attempts to attack submarines so far. The research revealed that, while the depth charges then in constant use were a great improvement on their predecessor, the anti-submarine bomb, they still lacked the precision and effectiveness to ensure a kill against a submarine. To improve the kill probability, the depth charges had to have either a more effective explosive charge or they had to be delivered to explode closer to the submarine. The pursuit of a more effective explosive was already under way, but the researchers also pointed out that most submarines attacked by aircraft were those either on the surface or just submerged. Even the depth charges delivered with great precision, straddling a submarine, would sink to between 100 and 150 feet before exploding. At such a depth they might shake a submarine but they would certainly not damage it severely.

PLATE 1.4. *Catalina* attacking U-boat. (*RAF Museum*)

Depth Charge Settings   Accordingly, the research section advised that the depth settings should be changed to ensure that the charges went off at 20 feet below the surface. Unfortunately, the basic depth charge was originally a naval weapon, designed for use from the decks of warships. It had a safety device ensuring that the minimum depth setting was 50 feet. Nevertheless, though not ideal, 50 feet was much closer than 150 and Coastal Command immediately began dropping depth charges with this setting. In parallel with this move, development began on a fusing device which would allow even shallower depths to be set: a shallow-setting hydrostatic pistol.

Intelligence   As well as operational aircrew, groundcrew, operations staff, weapon producers, research specialists and all those others engaged in putting effective aircraft and weapons in the right place to sink submarines, the intelligence officers played a significant part. Protection of British codes had not hitherto been very effective and it was quite early in the war that the German Navy broke the codes protecting the secret instructions to the British convoys.

However, a bigger and more far-reaching success was achieved when the British cracked the German *Enigma* codes and the associated machine cipher. The *Enigma* codes continued to be used by all of Germany's armed forces, and one of the most specific aims of the British security was to prevent the Germans from discovering that the codes had in fact been broken. As far as the German Navy was concerned, the code was a perfect vehicle for conveying all the signal traffic generated by the need to issue constant and comprehensive orders to the U-boats at sea. Doenitz's tactics of using his U-boats in packs demanded many precise orders and instructions to be transmitted and these were swiftly intercepted and decoded by British intelligence staffs.

Consequently, the tasking of British maritime aircraft for anti-submarine duties was more specific and accurate than ever it could have been without access to those orders. Naturally, because of errors and changes, it did not mean that every aircraft could fly to a specific point in the ocean and sink a U-boat. However, it certainly did mean that the aircraft could start its search in a much smaller area of sea.

Tactics   The lack of long-range aircraft meant that there was a gap of consider-able size in the Atlantic, where eastbound convoys left behind the air cover from the USA and Canada and sailed unprotected before coming within range of the British-based aircraft. Eventually the gap was plugged by the *Liberator* aircraft fitted with extra fuel tanks, but, before those aircraft were available, Coastal Command maintained the offensive and took the war to the submarines wherever it could reach them. Potentially the best chances of attacking submarines within range were to be had in the transit areas to and from the bases on the French Atlantic coast and the seas between Scotland and Iceland. Thus the Bay of Biscay became a permanent patrol area for the aircraft engaged in the hunt.

The in-service use of the airborne ASV radar had so far been disappointing and, once again, specific analysis of the problem and its causes revealed much that could be improved. The serviceability of the equipment was suffering through the poor training of ground staff and aircrews, there were insufficient spares, and operating the radar was unpopular because it was not a specific part of any one crew member's responsibilities. As before, rapid responses to these problems by improving training, providing spares, and making the operation of the radar a specific responsibility of the wireless operator, as well as ordering an extra such operator to fly on sorties where the ASV radar was to be used, all combined to produce much better results from the equipment.

The German Navy did not sit idle during these developments but concentrated efforts on equipment which could detect the ASV transmissions from aircraft. Since the transmissions could be detected at ranges beyond the capability of the aircraft to receive a reflected radar echo, the submarines could submerge and hide well before the aircraft got close enough to detect it either on radar or visually. This equipment, a basic radar warning receiver known as Metox, gave the U-boats adequate warning of the approach of a radar-equipped aircraft and accounted for the survival of many of the U-boats transiting the Bay of Biscay between September 1942 and January 1943.

Advanced Radar   The change in Allied fortunes in February 1943 was brought about once more by a technological advance. This time it was the introduction into service of the advanced centrimetric radar. Not only had time elapsed since its early development and trials but also the conflict of priorities between Bomber Command and Coastal Command had been overtaken by events, if not entirely solved. The new radar facilitated detection of submarines at greater ranges, as well as operating at a frequency which rendered it undetectable by the U-boat Metox equipment. Once more, the surfaced U-boat could be surprised by the sudden arrival of an attacking aircraft announced only by the glare of the Leigh Light in the final stage of weapon delivery. The Allied success, if not in sinking U-boats but certainly in harassing them, drove Doenitz to order his submarines crossing the Bay of Biscay to submerge at night and only surface during the day for the recharging of batteries.

As 1943 wore on, the picture in mid Atlantic, particularly in the Atlantic 'Gap', began to change. At first, Doenitz capitalised on his relative freedom from air attack in the area and ordered his submarines to form large hunting packs in which to molest the Allied convoys. In this they achieved successes when the weather allowed, and Allied losses were high. However, by May of that year, two *Liberator* squadrons were operational and these very long-range aircraft could reach the mid Atlantic with sufficient fuel to remain on patrol over the convoys for a worthwhile period. Furthermore, a new weapon had by then been introduced into front-line service: the homing torpedo, known by its unclassified title as the Mark 24 Mine.

The Torpedo   The principle of the homing device in the torpedo was essentially acoustic: a detector in the torpedo heard noise and was able to identify the direction of the source of it. Steering adjustments could then be made for the torpedo to guide itself direct to the noise and explode on impact with the source. A most interesting point, though, is that both sides started using the acoustic torpedoes at roughly the same time. The Germans, the British and the Americans all had separately been pursuing the same aim of producing an accurate and reliable homing torpedo and all had varying degrees of success with several different methods of homing. Gradually the acoustic homing method was left as the one most likely to achieve a successful homing, though several other solutions were tried.

The early recognition of effective countermeasures against the acoustic torpedo by deploying a decoy noise generator was significant in that it inspired further investigations of other homing devices. Nevertheless, it was the acoustic homing device which won the day and, for the Allies, it was the American version which entered service first: on 12 May 1943 a *Liberator* of No. 86 Squadron attacked U-456 with an acoustic homing torpedo. The torpedo exploded against the hull of the submerged U-boat, crippling her and forcing her to the surface. The boat was sunk the following day. The Germans first used their acoustic torpedoes in mid September 1943 in attacks against two convoys: the attacks accounted for two escort vessels' being sunk and the stern being blown off another.

PLATE 1.5. *Liberator* attacking U-boat. (*RAF Museum*)

Teamwork   As well as the advent of the long-range *Liberator* and the deployment of the air-launched, acoustic homing torpedo, a third factor was to play a decisive part in the role of aircraft in the anti-submarine war. This was the inclusion in the convoy escort forces of an escort carrier, equipped with offensive aircraft. Clearly much smaller than their land-based counterparts, and able to carry only smaller weapon loads, these aircraft and their crews nevertheless were effective against the U-boats. For instance, HMS *Biter* sailing with convoy HX 237 in May 1943 carried nine *Swordfish* and three *Wildcat* aircraft. While the *Swordfish* suffered losses from U-boat anti-aircraft fire, they were extremely successful in harassing the submarines, forcing them to dive before completing their attacks, then directing Allied surface escorts into accurate attacking positions.

By now, the fundamental importance of teamwork in anti-submarine warfare had been demonstrated many times over and firmly grasped: teamwork not only among the crew of an aircraft but also between separate aircraft, between aircraft and ships, between Air Force and Navy, between operational and intelligence staff, and between military and civilian researchers.

Measuring Success   For the Allies, success against the U-boats was not measured merely as numbers of submarines sunk. It was becoming widely accepted that, although sinking a U-boat was the ultimate aim and achieved the best long-term effect, harassing the Wolf Packs was just as lucrative. If the submarines could no longer press home their attack through being forced to submerge, then the convoys would enjoy safe passage. Although it was good news that several U-boats were sunk in mid-1943, it was even better news that Convoy HX 240 had reached Liverpool on 4 June 1943 and was the seventh successive convoy to have crossed the Atlantic completely unscathed. This welcome news was much more of an accurate indicator as to which way the Battle of the Atlantic was going. The German Navy could take only cold comfort from so many U-boat losses, set against virtually no gains in terms of Allied shipping sunk. But what Doenitz and Hitler himself remembered was that the Allies had been forced to invest tremendous resources and effort into the maritime war. Such an investment, had it not gone into the resources for the Battles of the Atlantic and of the Bay of Biscay, would surely have made a tremendous impact on the battles over mainland Europe.

The Schnorkel   Doenitz was becoming more convinced through his bitter experience of U-boat losses that what he needed were boats which could remain submerged for far longer than his current ones. Such U-boats would need a new propulsion system to obviate the necessity for surfacing regularly and frequently to recharge their batteries. Work was going ahead on such a propulsion system but was not proving to be successful. Meanwhile, an existing device was tested and pronounced satisfactory in achieving the aim of allowing the submarine to remain submerged while recharging its batteries. The device was a long breather tube which could be pushed above the surface while the boat was at periscope depth. Equipped with this so-called 'schnorkel', a boat could reap the benefits of plentiful supplies of fresh air while remaining submerged. This meant that the boat could run on its diesel engine and not use precious battery power.

It did suffer limitations in that the noise from the diesel engines prevented the U-boat crew from using them in an attack—first, the noise would have betrayed the presence of the U-boat, and secondly, it rendered their own listening equipment ineffective. Deploying the device also imposed restrictions on the submarine speed, which was reduced to about six knots in those circumstances. Although the schnorkel could be seen both visually and on radar when it was deployed, the detection ranges were much reduced as compared with those applicable to a surfaced submarine. The schnorkel was recognised as a great step in the right direction while the U-boat crews awaited the fruits of Doenitz's efforts for a new, improved submarine which could both transit at speed and attack while submerged.

Sound Underwater   These greater efforts to remain submerged drove the Allies to consider yet again the greatest weakness of the aircraft in anti-submarine warfare: aircrews had to rely on visual sightings which were denied once a submarine was submerged. Detection of submarines under the water had been successful with the use of systems reliant on the properties of sound waves in the water. It had been discovered many years previously that sound travels great distances through water, though the path of the sound waves was not always easily predictable. As early as the First World War, hydrophones had been suspended in the sea around the coast of Britain and listening posts ashore had successfully detected approaching submarines. A development of such a purely passive system was the introduction of active equipment which generated a sound pulse then waited for the return echo, which would denote the presence of an object in the water. As mentioned earlier, many Royal Navy ships were fitted with such a device, ASDIC, at the outbreak of war.

For aircraft, though, an effective capability to listen for tell-tale sounds in the ocean was to take a little longer to develop. Indeed, the idea had been tried in the First World War when seaplanes and flying boats were fitted with hydrophones. The craft would settle on the surface then deploy the hydrophones and listen. The first attempts were with non-directional hydrophones and the results were very poor. Even when a directional hydrophone was fitted and tried it proved ineffective. Deploying the system entailed stopping the engines, which the aircrews were reluctant to do. Also, the range of the hydrophones was very short, usually less than several hundred yards. Thus the aircraft and hydrophone combination did not achieve anything operationally in the First World War.

Developments with Sound and Aircraft   By the early part of the Second World War there was renewed emphasis on linking the detection capability of a sonar system with the speed and flexibility of an aircraft. Again, leading on from the development of sonar systems on board ships, the suggestion that aircraft might drop directional hydrophones from their bomb racks then listen in to the results broadcast on high-frequency radio was not long in coming. The idea was vigorously pursued in America and in January 1942 the project of a 'Bomb buoy' was started. The device was to be dropped from an aircraft and would descend by parachute into the water.

Once in the water, the hydrophone would sink to a depth of 20 feet and the buoy would broadcast high-frequency signals to the listening aircraft. After the battery run-down time had elapsed, usually about four hours, a soluble plug would dissolve and the buoy would sink. The limitation of these sonobuoys was their short range, and such a feature demanded that the buoys be placed as close to the submarine as possible before being able to pass usable information. Thus there was a requirement for the submarine to be first detected by some other means, then and only then could sonobuoys be deployed to generate more information on the position, course and speed of the submarine.

A Combination of Sensors   The other detection means were radar or visual sightings, but they were, of course, unable to detect submarines under water. Nevertheless, through application and no little skill, with a combination of sensors and weapon, some successful attacks were completed. For example, on 20 March 1945 the crew of the *Liberator* operating near the Orkneys were alerted by their radar operator that he had detected a suspicious contact some three miles away. The crew flew to the object but as they approached, radar contact was lost and the visual lookouts could see nothing in the fading light. Carrying neither flares nor searchlight, the crew were unable to illuminate the area but they decided to drop a pattern of five sonobuoys.

The acoustics operator was soon able to confirm that his sonobuoys were indeed detecting and transmitting back to the aircraft the tell-tale sound of a submarine propeller. Deciphering the various signals from each sonobuoy, the crew could make a reasonable though rough estimate of where the U-boat was. The radar operator suddenly got a short return from the top of a schnorkel painting on his screen. Equipped with just these two pieces of information from radar and sonobuoys, the crew only had a vague idea of where the submarine might be. Even knowing that their acoustic homing torpedoes had to be dropped close enough to the target to be able to detect it, they pressed ahead with an attack and released their torpedoes over the most likely position.

After about six minutes, the operator heard the swishing noises of the propeller, then to be overlaid by a long, booming sound. As that sound died away, there was nothing to be heard but sea noises. Although the crew could see nothing outside the aircraft, they claimed a kill on their return and post-war analysis of German records confirmed that a U-boat had indeed disappeared without trace at about that time.

Magnetic Anomaly Detection   Despite such successes, for there were others, the sonobuoy was not considered effective enough to be an aid to the underwater searching of the open ocean. Other methods, apart from acoustics, were explored, and the most successful was the exploitation of the magnetic properties of the earth and large metal objects. The magnetic anomaly (or airborne in the early days) detector (MAD) was an aircraft-mounted device which, through its sensitive magnetometers, could detect a distortion of the earth's magnetic field caused by the metal body of a submarine. Again, there was a severe limitation on the use of the equipment in that it was useful only at short ranges, of the order of 600 feet.

Magnetic Anomaly Detection in the Mediterranean   However, unlike the sonobuoys, there was one place where MAD could be used as an initial detection device. The German presence across Europe and on down to Africa meant that the Mediterranean was another deployment area for U-boats. The biggest drawback to operations in the Mediterranean was that U-boats sailing in from the Atlantic had to pass through the Straits of Gibraltar. Owing to the natural features of the Straits, the very deep but very narrow channel, only four miles wide, and the contrary currents flowing through it, submarines sailing eastwards would most likely be at depths of between 100 and 150 feet. Furthermore, German tactics recommended that U-boats traversed the Straits submerged during daylight hours, having recharged their batteries the previous night.

All these factors combined to give an American squadron with MAD-fitted *Catalinas* the best chance of using MAD only to detect submarines. The *Catalina* patrols, consisting of tight, four-mile long orbits across the channel, were flown at 100 feet. Having two aircraft perpetually on such orbits all through the daylight hours was a virtual guarantee that U-boats would be found. The ploy on detection was to attempt to track the submarine by criss-crossing the area and dropping smoke markers at each 'MAD mark' to construct a line on the water denoting the course and speed of the submarine. Once the *Catalina* crews were satisfied that they had sufficient information for an attack, they would fly down the line of smoke markers.

PLATE 1.6. *Catalina.* (*RAF Museum*)

On detecting another MAD mark, indicating that the aircraft was again over the submarine, the crew would fire retro bombs—bombs launched backwards to overcome the effect of the aircraft speed and thus fall into the water close to the point where the magnetic anomaly was detected. Other measures open to the *Catalina* crews were to call on the surface ships in the area to assist in the attack and lend their firepower to the effort to sink the U-boat. The surface ships themselves, although on constant patrol, were severely hampered by the fickle conditions in the Mediterranean where the shipborne sonar was frequently severely degraded.

The Type XXI U-Boat   In the persistent dark cloud of these losses, Doenitz pinned his hopes not only on the continued bravery, determination and loyalty of his U-boat crews, but also on the development of a new, larger submarine. Known as the Type XXI, it was to be the best answer to the domination of the seas by Allied aircraft and navies. With the ability to remain submerged for long periods and travel underwater at high speeds, it was to be a severe threat to the Allied convoys by exploiting the weakness in the Allied capability: no large area-detection capability against submerged submarines.

However, the introduction into service of the Type XXI was severely delayed by RAF bombing of the construction yards, the railway network and the assembly areas on mainland Europe. So much so that the Allies overran Germany and forced the end of the war before the Type XXI could fire a torpedo against a convoy. It remains a questionable point whether the Type XXI would have dramatically reversed the fortunes of the Germans or whether it would merely have delayed the end of the war by just a few months. It certainly would have been a potent weapon in the hands of Admiral Doenitz.

PLATE 1.7. Type XXI U-boat. (*RAF Museum*)

The Man in the Machine   In considering the see-saw type of swing of the advantage from one side to the other, based mainly on technological development, it is all too easy to overlook the often prime factor of the contribution of people. No amount of technology could have achieved the aim had it not been for the bravery, skill, determination and patience of the aircrews engaged in anti-submarine warfare. Patrols looking for submarines would more often than not be long, tedious, difficult and seemingly fruitless, conducted many miles from home in rough weather and over an extremely inhospitable ocean. The equipment needed careful and meticulous handling if even the most rudimentary results were to be obtained. And, most crucial of all, U-boats caught on the surface always had the option of staying to fight it out. Armed with effective anti-aircraft guns they could make life very difficult and dangerous for the crew of a maritime aircraft pressing home an attack. Many U-boats were forced or elected to choose this option and survived the air attack while inflicting lethal damage on the aircraft and aircrew.

Anti-Surface Unit Warfare   While the war against the submarines was being fought by the long-range patrol aircraft, other aircraft were engaged in attacks against surface shipping. However, the distinction between anti-submarine and anti-surface warfare in the Second World War is necessarily blurred because of the submarine's preference for travelling long distances on the surface. Furthermore, long-range aircraft were used against surface ships when necessary. The main aircraft used in anti-shipping attacks were the *Hudson*, the *Beaufort* and the *Beaufighter*, though later in the war the *Mosquito* and even the *Typhoon* were used to great effect. The weapons employed against the ships were air-launched torpedoes, bombs, rockets and cannon.

To deliver the air-launched torpedo, the crews were required to fly a steady non-manoeuvring course towards the target at low level and at reasonable speed. The torpedoes were heavy and long in the body and thus vulnerable to breaking up on hitting the water if dropped too high or too fast. So that the weapon did not explode on impact with the sea, and thus damage the delivery aircraft, there was a delayed fusing device which prevented the arming of the explosive until after several turns of the torpedo propeller in the water. However, the delivery pattern did render the aircraft vulnerable to shipborne defences, like anti-aircraft artillery, and ship attacks were deemed to be very dangerous.

Similarly, for bomb and gun attacks where the aircraft flew even closer to the ships to ensure a greater accuracy of weapon delivery, the ship's gunners were presented with large aircraft targets at close ranges. Nevertheless, aircraft were invariably included in the list of forces employed against large surface vessels because of their speed of reaction, range and firepower.

The Importance of Intelligence   The major question in the pursuit of naval shipping was always location: where is the enemy and where is he going? The threat of what capital ships could do if allowed to roam the Atlantic unhindered was enormous and spurred the Royal Navy and the Royal Air Force into greater efforts to find and destroy German ships such as the *Scharnhorst*, the *Lutzöw*, the *Prinze Eugen*, the *Gniesenau* and the *Tirpitz*. But finding the ships was not easy and the fall of Norway increased the problem enormously. With the facility to leave German waters, stay close to Denmark then head for the Norwegian coast and remain in a number of Norwegian fiord hideouts for as long as necessary, the German ships could avoid detection and remain in safe water until the time was ripe for a dash to the open seas and the rich pickings of the Atlantic Ocean.

Operations against the Scharnhorst   The task of the RAF aircrews was, first, to patrol the Norwegian coastal waters on surface surveillance and report any ships sighted. Secondly, having found a ship and having reported the position back to the maritime headquarters, the aircrew were to attack. In this way, it was intended that the German ships should not have the freedom of movement and should be sunk if possible. The attacks against the *Scharnhorst* in June 1940 were typical: two *Blenheim* reconnaissance aircraft of RAF Coastal Command located the German battle-cruiser together with her accompanying destroyers at anchor off Trondheim. *Hudsons* were directed to attack the ship but low cloud prevented accurate location of the target. This remained for some time but after six days, the *Scharnhorst* was reported to be steaming south.

PLATE 1.8. *Hudson.* (*RAF Museum*)

Blenheims and a *Sunderland* were ordered out to locate and shadow the ship but the *Blenheims* were engaged *en route* by a Heinkel and a Dornier. Thus, the *Sunderland* pressed on alone and eventually sighted the *Scharnhorst* with her escorts. The crew signalled base with the location report and a force of *Beauforts*, *Hudsons* and *Swordfish*, already despatched to attack the ship, altered course to make for a new intercept position.

The continuing task of the *Sunderland*, to stay in contact with the German ships, was made extremely hazardous by the anti-aircraft fire directed at it. The first of the attack aircraft on the scene were six Royal Navy *Swordfish* who dived to achieve a release position for their torpedoes. The aircraft encountered a tremendous barrage of fire and one was hit, burst into flames and crashed into the sea. The others pressed on and launched their torpedoes before turning away and beginning a zigzag escape manoeuvre to avoid more gunfire.

Once again the German guns turned on the *Sunderland*. The issue was worsened by the arrival of first a Heinkel 60 seaplane, which attempted to aim a bomb at the *Sunderland*. The bomb missed, but next to arrive, and potentially much more lethal, was a flight of four Messerschmitt 109 fighters. On this occasion, though, the fighters did not capitalise on their superiority in speed, agility and numbers. Instead, they preferred to remain at long range, firing ineffective bursts at the *Sunderland*. If they came close enough to the patrol aircraft, the *Sunderland's* own guns returned fire accurately and damaged the fighters, eventually sending one of them into the sea in flames. The remaining fighters then left the scene and, shortly afterwards, the lone *Sunderland* departed for base, being at the limit of its fuel-dictated endurance time.

The *Beaufort* formation was next on the scene, nine aircraft in three flights of three. The *Beauforts* usually carried torpedoes, and the ships, on recognising the aircraft type, deployed into an anti-torpedo formation. However, on this occasion the *Beauforts* were each armed with two heavy, armour-piercing bombs. At least three of the bombs scored direct hits on the cruiser and machine-gun fire was ranged across the destroyers. None of the ships damaged the *Beauforts* with their anti-aircraft fire and the bombers regrouped for their return home. They were not to escape unscathed, though, as by now they were under attack from a large group of Messerschmitt fighters from bases in Norway. The *Beauforts* persisted in their efforts to reach home safely but lost three of their formation while destroying at least one fighter.

Hudsons bombing from high level made further attacks on the *Scharnhorst*, but the results were unknown because of the anti-aircraft fire from the ships. The combination of attacks from the *Swordfish*, the *Beauforts* and the *Hudsons* had certainly damaged the battle-cruiser but had not sunk her. Nevertheless, the action was deemed effective because of the severe limitations it imposed on the activities of the *Scharnhorst*.

Curtailment and Co-operation   The *Lutzöw* (previously known as the *Deutschland*) was engaged in actions which also proved that it was not necessary to sink a ship in order to curtail her activities. Having been found by a *Blenheim*, the *Lutzöw* was attacked by three *Beauforts* with torpedoes and was subsequently seen limping back to port, trailing oil. However, the bottling-up of capital ships was not without mishap, and it was a severe blow to discover in February 1942 that the *Scharnhorst* and the *Gniesenau* together with the *Prinz Eugen* had slipped out of Brest harbour and were *en route* to Germany via the English Channel. The convoy was lost and found several times in the foul weather but was eventually attacked by *Swordfish*, *Beauforts* and *Hudsons*. Although inconclusive, these attacks were pressed home in the face of intense fire. They were also evidence of the co-operation between the Royal Air Force and the Royal Navy in pursuing and attacking these large surface units, which were so potentially threatening to Allied

PLATE 1.9. *Beaufort*. (*RAF Museum*)

convoys. Another example of co-operation was the sinking of the *Bismarck* which was located by aircraft and subsequently trailed by them in a long chase before being eventually sunk by naval gunfire.

Lessons Learnt   As the German naval units were either penned in to various harbours or ultimately sunk, the attentions of the aircraft designed for attacks on surface shipping were turned towards ports or to the steady flow of supply shipping between Germany, the Danish waters and Norway. Early experiences had brought out several lessons: accurate and up to date knowledge of the position of the surface ships was vital; accurate delivery of the weapons, be they torpedoes or bombs entailed approaching very low and very close to the ships; but such an extremely low level of approach put the aircraft in a most vulnerable position because of fire from the ship's defences; survival of the aircraft in the face of fighter escorts over the ship could be enhanced by employing fighters to accompany the bombers; and, finally, it was not necessary to sink a ship in order to prevent it from performing its war role.

Putting these principles into practice was not always possible, particularly the provision of fighters to go with the bombers. Indeed, in the three months up to July 1942, the casualty rates showed that 25% of the attacking aircraft had been shot down. The Commander in Chief of Coastal Command ordered a cessation of low-level attacks, preferring his crews to approach at medium levels. Immediately the casualty rates diminished, but then, understandably, the number of ships sunk also fell dramatically. Nevertheless, the anti-shipping role was pursued with some vigour and an 'East Coast Striking Force' was even formed of *Hudsons* and *Beauforts*. Continually the balance between the need for accurate, effective attack and the requirement not to lose every aircraft to defensive guns was being weighed. Again, the bravery, determination and skill of the aircrews played a vital part in the equation.

In one attempt to provide slightly greater stand-off from the targets, the aircraft were equipped with rockets. Later still, some *Mosquitoes* were armed with a six-pounder anti-tank gun to provide not only some stand-off but also greater hitting power. A *Mosquito* equipped with this 40-rounds-a-minute gun hit and damaged a U-boat which was on the surface returning to its French base in October 1943. Another returning U-boat was actually sunk by a pair of *Mosquitoes* in March 1944 when rounds from the heavy calibre weapon penetrated the pressure hull. The advantages of the *Mosquito* were not limited to firepower: the speed and agility of the aircraft meant that it was more than a match for the defensive systems allotted to these U-boats, whether the systems were German fighter aircraft or heavily armed converted merchant ships.

PLATE 1.10. *Mosquito* attacking submarine. (*RAF Museum*)

Targets of Opportunity   One short period of successful attacks by aircraft against submarines on the surface occurred between April and the end of the war in May 1945. Owing to a unique combination of circumstances, 26 submarines were sunk. The factors which combined to produce such results were the fall of the Baltic States to Russia, necessitating the withdrawal of the U-boats from their bases; the enforced transit of the U-boats from the Baltic via the Kattegat *en route* to Norway; the shallow seas in the area which forced the U-boats to transit on the surface; the proximity of airfields now held by the Allies; and the complete absence of any German air effort to protect the U-boats or at least harass the attacking Allies.

Faced with the opportunities created by such favourable conditions, the Allies were not slow to extract the maximum capital. A formation of *Mosquitoes* equipped with rockets sank three U-boats on one day. Owing particularly to the lack of German fighter cover, the Allied heavy aircraft joined the fray most effectively, as did *Typhoon* fighter-bombers, which accounted for at least eight U-boats. As such a unique set of circumstances is unlikely to recur, there are few implications to be drawn from this 'target-rich' period, other than perhaps to highlight the basic need to capitalise swiftly on any opportunity which presents itself.

Aerial Mine Laying   One method of attacking both ships and submarines lacked the advantages of immediate visible gains and results, but was nevertheless an extremely effective way of inflicting damage without losing friendly aircraft: laying anti-shipping mines. Developing the advantages of aircraft in such a role was straightforward, and the speed of laying, the flexibility of decision as to where to lay, and the long ranges from Britain accessible to planners all determined that aircraft could be efficiently employed. Indeed, even Bomber Command aircraft could be ordered into mine-laying operations on those nights when the bombing of mainland Europe was impracticable. One significant example of a successful mining campaign was the restriction imposed on the German training of U-boat crews. Such training was generally accomplished in the Baltic but after the sea was sown with mines, three U-boats were sunk and others harassed and hampered by necessary mine countermeasures. Thus aircraft contributed in many ways to the successful campaign against German maritime assets.

Maritime Air Defence

Capabilities   During the Second World War, the distinction between the roles of maritime air defence and anti-submarine warfare or anti-surface unit warfare was far from clear. As we have already seen, for example, the *Sunderland* flying boat could be just as lethal against aircraft like the ME 109 as against a submarine. Admiral Doenitz saw part of the solution as taking the offensive against the aircraft which were proving so effective against his precious packs of submarines. He asked for the Heinkel 177, a twin-engined bomber with sufficient range and armament to reconnoitre the Atlantic convoys and attack Allied aircraft in the Bay of Biscay. The HE 177s were not available to him until October 1943 and even then they were ineffective.

Move and Counter-Move However, to meet his demands for retaliation against the RAF and Commonwealth aircraft, he was given a squadron of Junkers 88C-6s which were generally very effective. In October 1942 the JU 88s destroyed 16 RAF aircraft, but the RAF were quick to respond and squadrons of _Beaufighters_ were being formed in interceptor wings. The _Beaufighters_ were themselves successful and shot down many Focke Wulf 200s, the convoy-shadowing aircraft, as well as the JU 88s ostensibly protecting German convoys and U-boats.

PLATE 1.11. _Beaufighter._ (_RAF Museum_)

A Combined Operation Other examples of maritime air defence and air superiority include the air action over the Norwegian island of Vaagsö in December 1941, when all three services combined in an operation to destroy German installations on the island and also to sink 16,000 tons of shipping. Coastal Command were given the task of protecting the destroyers as they waited offshore for the Commandos. The aircraft were then to prolong the protection by escorting the destroyers back to Britain.

Blenheim fighters and the _Beaufighters_ circled the island as the Commando raids took their toll and when Messerschmitts and Heinkels arrived to threaten the destroyers, the fighters engaged immediately. Not one bomb hit a ship and four bombers were shot down, although not without price; three British aircraft did not return.

Principles   The development of maritime air defence in the Second World War was thus another see-saw motion, determined by action and re-action on the part of both the Germans and the Allies. The principles which quickly emerged were that co-ordination of all participating forces was paramount; aircraft with long range and effective firepower were needed; speed and agility were also necessary; and that significant forces should be allotted to the task. Eventually, towards the end of the war, as has already been described, the anti-shipping aircraft could operate with complete freedom of action since there was little or no opposition posed by the Luftwaffe over German naval units.

Air–Sea Rescue   It will come as no surprise to discover that the rescue of downed airmen or shipwrecked seamen was conducted by many surface, sub-surface and air units and that any one rescue usually combined the efforts of some if not all three types. The role played by land-based, fixed-wing aircraft was generally that of location, i.e., searching an area and finding survivors and then directing a ship or launch to the position to pick them up. On the other hand, the *Sunderland* and the *Catalina* flying boat were naturally capable, weather permitting, of landing on the water beside the dinghy or lifeboat and themselves picking up those in distress. Rescues were not confined to one side, but anyone out in a dinghy, Allied or German, were considered worthy of rescue.

The Air–Sea Rescue Service ran co-ordinated activities from February 1941 and, by the beginning of 1944, possessed 32 marine craft units, as well as directing search squadrons which had a variety of aircraft, including the Supermarine *Walrus*. From February 1941 to December 1943, the Air–Sea Rescue Service had rescued 3,306 Allied airmen, mainly from the North Sea and the English Channel.

One Successful Rescue   One of many thousands of rescues occurred when a Heinkel was shot down over the North Sea. The Coastal Command Operations Room received the report, including the indication that there were probably survivors in the water. A high-speed launch was despatched from a nearby fishing port and made contact with a *Hudson* which had already arrived on the scene and had begun a search. The *Hudson* was unable to find a dinghy but the launch crew spotted a man in the water supported by his life jacket. The launch rescued the Heinkel pilot and returned to shore.

Equipment and Principles   Land-based aircraft were fitted with several items of equipment to drop to survivors while directing surface vessels to the rescue. Such items included packs of warm clothing, food, water, and even a small boat, eventually to be replaced by a larger inflatable dinghy. Again, the principles to be observed in sustaining an efficient rescue service soon emerged: a rapid reaction to the first news of people in the water or in a dinghy was vital; clear communications between all units and the directing headquarters was essential; the units themselves needed accurate navigational gear to begin their search of the right area; long-range aircraft were necessary to conduct long searches far from land; and an old but fundamental truth was that crews involved in intensive visual searches would tire quickly.

THE LINK WITH THE PRESENT

These illustrations from the history of the Second World War show the way in which specific guidelines and principles evolved to dictate the shape and conduct of maritime air operations today. As we move on to more detailed descriptions of each of the current disciplines, it will be clear that most of those guidelines and principles are still being applied.

2

Anti-Submarine Warfare

CONTROL OF THE ATLANTIC

The U-boats of Admiral Doenitz played a significant part in the Second World War. They presented such a threat to Allied merchant shipping crossing the Atlantic that vast resources were invested in the means to defeat them. The spur to such investment and development was the importance of the materials being transported across the ocean in Allied convoys. In any projected future war in Europe, the movement of materials and men from the USA to the United Kingdom would be of more, not less, importance. Notwithstanding the presence of forces already in Europe, the subsequent reinforcement before, then during any conflict would be vital to success.

In September 1989, Admiral Frank B. Kelso II, US Navy, the Supreme Allied Commander Atlantic, described the Atlantic reinforcement and resupply of NATO as the Alliance's centre of gravity, using von Clausewitz's definition of 'a centre of gravity' as the hub of all power and movement, on which everything depends. Admiral Kelso went on to point out that it was clear that the current Soviet leadership understood very clearly their unchallenged conventional military position in Europe, unless North America is able to come to the defence of Europe. North America would be unable to come to its defence without control of the Atlantic.

THE REQUIREMENT FOR ANTI-SUBMARINE WARFARE

One of the essential criteria in establishing control of the Atlantic would be the waging of a successful anti-submarine warfare (ASW) campaign. But, in contrast to the situation in the Second World War, protection of Allied convoys is not the only reason why an anti-submarine warfare campaign should form a fundamental part of the maritime strategy. Modern submarines are not confined to attacks against surface shipping. On the contrary, their development has progressed so far that there are now several quite distinct types of submarine, the most significant of which is the ballistic nuclear missile carrier. These types of submarine are strategic weapon systems with the advantages of being able to remain undetected until required, to roam to unpredictable positions, then to fire large loads of nuclear missiles with extreme precision. Other submarines are equipped for long-range conventional attacks against land targets, and yet more are employed in the anti-submarine role themselves. Another essential facet of maritime operations would therefore be to gain control of the Norwegian Sea by anti-submarine warfare and thereby deny the use of that sea to enemy submarines.

The Aim

Anti-submarine warfare has therefore a vital part to play in any national or alliance strategy. The success of an ASW campaign is not measured merely in terms of enemy submarines sunk, but in an assessment of how the submarines are being prevented from achieving their own aims, be they attacks against surface ships or deployments into missile-firing positions. This again illustrates the diversity of submarine roles and therefore the diversity required of a modern strategy for ASW. Nevertheless, the aim of anti-submarine warfare is to deny to the enemy the effective use of his submarines. To consider how a nation might wish to make effective use of its submarines we should consider in detail an actual submarine fleet. Because of the sheer size and diversity of their fleet, we shall examine the Soviet submarines.

Furthermore, the Soviet naval forces will bear close examination despite recent international events. Although there are great moves towards arms reductions, a Conventional Force in Europe agreement on naval arms limitations is not yet envisaged. Also, the USSR has shown no inclination to reduce its submarine fleet. Even a peaceable, introspective USSR is likely to retain the world's biggest submarine fleet and therefore the shape and capabilities of that fleet will strongly influence the development of anti-submarine warfare. Just as importantly, many Third World countries will develop their own submarine capabilities and some are likely either to buy Soviet submarines or to apply Soviet submarine technology to their own boats.

THE SOVIET SUBMARINE FLEET

Conventional Power with Nuclear Weapons

Long recognised as the architect of the present Soviet Navy, Fleet Admiral Gorshkov was the Commander in Chief for over 25 years. One of his clearest statements was in differentiating between fleet versus fleet, and fleet versus shore operations. By fleet versus shore he meant the strategic use of nuclear force from the sea against the vital parts of an opponent. It was in 1955 that the first Soviet-launched nuclear ballistic missile was tested and by 1957 this SS-N-4 (Submarine-Nuclear-4: a NATO designation) with a 300-mile range and a megaton warhead was deployed at sea in the conventional, but specially converted, *Zulu* class submarine. This paved the way for the appearance in 1958 of the *Golf* class, another conventionally-powered boat which could carry three missiles but which had to surface to fire them. The type had many limitations and was required to come to the surface in waters dominated by American forces if it was to fire its missiles and they were to reach their potential targets. These limitations meant that the *Golf* class did not set up a regular patrol pattern.

Nuclear Power

After these experiences, all subsequent strategic missile firers were nuclear powered. The first of these was the *Hotel* class, which was little different from the *Golf* in capability: it carried only three missiles and also had to surface to fire. However, by 1964 the vessels had been modified and equipped to fire missiles from under the surface with ranges up to 750 nautical miles. While making these advances, the Soviets were still dogged by other problems: their boats were noisy, the power plants were unreliable and the ranges of the missiles were so short as to dictate long transits to patrol areas dangerously close to the USA.

Greater Range

The next type of boat, the *Yankee* class, carried more missiles, up to 16, with a range of 1,500 miles but these still demanded long transits and they were persistently noisy. Thus the Western detection rate was high and the Soviets were not prepared to deploy them in large numbers. However, with the *Delta* class, deployed in the 1970s, the Soviets at last had a missile system which could reach the continental United States from patrol positions in the Barents and the Okhotsk Sea. From these waters, which could be rendered relatively safe by Soviet ASW forces, the potential of a reliable strategic weapon system was realised. The NATO abbreviation for a nuclear submarine armed with ballistic missiles, the SSBN, was justifiably applied.

The Russian development did not stop there but surged on to bigger and better boats with the launch in 1980 of the first of the *Typhoon*-class submarines. This submarine is enormous and is reported to carry 20 SS-N-20 missiles with the capability of being launched underwater, a range of 4,500 nautical miles and warheads of the multiple independently targeted re-entry vehicle type. With a reported beam dimension of 75 feet there is a strong likelihood that the boat has a double hull and therefore many advantages in terms of survivability and protection.

Another feature is that the hulls are made of a titanium alloy and are thus even harder to penetrate. While the Russians seem to favour operating their ballistic missile-firers from oceans which they can themselves defend, such strength in the *Typhoon* may indicate an acceptance that even those defences might be penetrated. On the other hand, the strength of the *Typhoon* may be a manifestation of a desire for a flexible weapon system which might as easily be operated from out in the open ocean as from the bastions off the Kola Peninsula.

Other Factors Influencing Submarine Design

Other factors were also at work in determining the design and capability of Russian submarines, apart from the need to develop a secure strategic missile launch system. For use against surface ships, be they naval units or merchantmen, the work of the Germans up to 1945 had laid the foundations for Russian submarines of the *Whiskey* and the *Zulu* class. A medium range boat of about 1,000 tons, the *Whiskey* was conventional in that it had diesel and electric propulsion, and torpedoes as armament, as well as the snort necessary for operating the diesels while submerged. The only thing about these boats which was nuclear was the warhead on some of the torpedoes. The *Zulu* was capable of a higher underwater speed than the *Whiskey* and had a longer cruising range. But development of these rather slow, certainly noisy boats was relinquished after the perception of the threat to the Soviet homeland from the *Polaris*-equipped Western submarines and also from the United States' carrier battle groups. Any commander contemplating action against a well-armed, well-protected and fast moving carrier needed a range of weapon systems in his armoury. One such weapon could be the submarine, provided that submarine was itself fast and well-armed.

The Russian system which met these criteria, albeit somewhat crudely, was the *November*-class submarine. Although it was noisy and not very reliable, its nuclear propulsion made it fast and it was equipped with eight forward and two rear torpedo tubes. Naturally, the Soviets did not stop there: the *Victor* class which entered service in 1968, was their first tear-drop shaped submarine. This sort of hull form improves the strength, manoeuvrability and the flow of the submarine and the *Victor* was a significant step forward in hull design. Although still noisy compared to its Western counterparts, it was nevertheless a beginning on the long road to quieter Soviet submarines. The *Victor* has been well developed with the latest version, the *Victor* III, capable of 30 kts submerged, equipped with six torpedo tubes and the SS-N-15 ASW weapon. This latter weapon illustrates the point that the *Victor* III may not only be destined for anti-carrier operations, but has also a definite anti-submarine role. The blurring of responsibilities between specific types of Soviet submarines is commonplace.

Nuclear and Diesel/Electric Power

The advantages of nuclear-powered boats over their conventional counterparts are numerous: they can remain submerged for long periods and can transit at much higher speeds. The nuclear submarines are generally much more spacious and comfortable for their crews and long cruises may be borne with ease. However, these masterpieces of nautical engineering do have some drawbacks. They do create noise from the propulsion system and coolant pumps, and even nuclear submarines need to put up masts occasionally for communication or targeting. But the greatest drawback to the nuclear submarine is their enormous cost. Consequently, although diesel/electric submarines do have limitations in their needing to snort regularly, development of their basic types has continued at a swift pace. Diesel/electric submarines are far cheaper, far less complicated to operate, and do not invite the political problems associated with nuclear power. Furthermore, once submerged and operating on battery power, the diesel/electric submarine is still much quieter than all but the most modern nuclear submarines.

Thus the Soviet development of diesel/electric boats continued with the entry into service of the torpedo-armed *Foxtrot*, a reliable workhorse which was in production until 1972. The *Foxtrot* has six forward and four aft torpedo tubes and a submerged speed of 16 knots. The successor to the *Foxtrot* was the diesel/electric *Tango*, a smoother, quieter submarine with a better hull form. Another submarine with an advanced hull form was the *Kilo*, which first appeared in 1981. Although displacing some 3,000 tons submerged, this boat is only 220 feet long and is therefore quite short and broad, even complying with Western ideas of modern hull design.

Mixed Capabilities

This variety of types of submarine together comprises an arsenal of some 200 boats spread across the Northern, the Baltic, the Black Sea and the Pacific Fleet. As well as ballistic missiles for strategic attacks and torpedoes for assaults on surface vessels, it quickly became clear that technology would also provide the capability for submarines to fire shorter-range missiles, aimed at surface units. At first these missiles were rather large pilotless aircraft and the complete weapon system operated under several disadvantages. The submarine had to surface to fire and the targeting information was provided by a third party, usually a reconnaissance aircraft. Establishing communication between the submarine and the aircraft was always difficult and the aircraft was itself usually under threat from surface units. Even when these problems had been overcome and the missiles were eventually launched towards their targets, a lethal hit on the surface unit was by no means a foregone conclusion. The surface unit could detect the approach of a missile and could jam or seduce the homing head. Although these early anti-ship missile boats, the *Echo* and *Juliet* classes, were produced in some number and their presence posed a threat, the surface units likely to be targeted always reckoned they had some chance of defeating the system.

It is different with the *Charlie* class, the successor to the *Echo* and *Juliet*. The *Charlie* carries, and can fire submerged, eight missiles of a shorter range. These two factors, firing submerged and shorter-range missiles, mean that the *Charlie* would probably attack the surface targets as an independent weapon system, having found and tracked them while submerged. But relying on third-party targeting has not been abandoned, as the *Oscar* class submarine, first launched in 1980, carried missiles with a 250-nautical mile range and probably relies on satellite information with which to target the ships. The relatively new missiles fly a profile much closer to the surface of the sea and are smaller, thus reducing their chances of being detected.

Submarine versus Submarine

And finally in this short survey of Soviet submarines, and bearing in mind the danger of being too specific about which type conducts what sort of operation, there are those boats which appear to be designed for submarine versus submarine operations. The *Alfa* class was first launched in 1970 with properties which made it quite remarkable. The hull was probably built of a titanium alloy and therefore had great strength and crush resistance. Accordingly Western calculations put the theoretical crushing depth of this submarine at beneath 2,000 feet. It also had a new nuclear-powered propulsion plant and was credited with a speed of 42 kts, enough to catch the attention of Western crews of submarines and surface vessels alike. The anti-submarine weapons carried by the *Alfa* comprise the wire-guided torpedo and the tube-launched SS-N-15 missile with a final stage weapon of either a lightweight torpedo or a nuclear depth bomb.

The other class appearing to be specifically designed for anti-submarine work is the *Victor* III, armed with weapons similar to those on the *Alfa* class. The *Victor* III has a streamline casing for speed and quietening and also a large pod mounted on the tail fin. There are conflicting theories as to the nature of this pod: one school believes it to be the housing for a towed array sonar system for the long-range detection of submerged submarines. However, another doubts this theory by suggesting that the pod is too small to house a winching or winding gear to deploy and recover the towed array. Furthermore, it believes that the fin is too weak to provide the required anchorage for such a system. The opinion of the second school is that the pod houses some form of supplementary propulsion, designed to provide sufficient power to move the submarine at speeds less than about seven knots, but very quietly. To add to the problems of Western anti-submarine warfare forces, both the *Alfa* and the *Victor* III have special extra coatings on their hulls to reduce the reflection of sonar echoes from active sonar systems. Successors to the *Victor* III have already been identified as the *Sierra* and the *Akula* class, both also equipped with a fin-mounted pod.

Capabilities and Intentions

Thus the Soviet fleets of submarines are capable of performing many functions, and the probable intentions of the Soviets in any major conflict would capitalise on those abilities. Nevertheless, there is still doubt as to how much effort they would apportion to each role. The pattern of peacetime deployments comprise just two main subdivisions of activity: permanently maintained patrol stations and exercise deployments. The patrol stations include up to 10 submarines in the Mediterranean, three in the Indian Ocean and up to 12 ballistic missile-firers out 'on patrol'. There may be up to 50 boats out in the open oceans for major training on exercises.

The aim for the patrolling submarines seems to be to gain and maintain contact on large Western carrier battle groups and submarines. The Soviet forces should then be able to convert swiftly into an attacking position should war break out. Such activities would primarily be conducted against those Western naval units, surface units or submarines, which are perceived to present a threat to the Soviet homeland. Those great instruments of a forward maritime strategy and power projection, the American carrier battle groups, would always attract the attentions of a force of Soviet submarines whenever deployed to the north Norwegian seas. Similarly, Western ballistic missile submarines when on patrol must generate a large amount of interest. The difference between these two potential target groups is that, whereas the Soviet submarines could trail a carrier battle group, if not alone then certainly with help from other sources, there is well-founded scepticism as to whether the Soviets have ever had more than a fleeting glimpse of a Western ballistic missile submarine.

As tension mounts, it is likely that the Soviets would concentrate their submarines in areas where they could protect their own missile firers, such as the so-called 'bastions' off the Kola Peninsula. They would also have submarines in positions likely to be able to intercept and halt the approach of large Allied forces, such as the carrier battle groups. And, undoubtedly, the Soviets would despatch a force of submarines, however small, to disrupt the Allied sea lines of communication, particularly the Atlantic reinforcement routes.

OTHER SUBMARINE FLEETS

Such, then, is the force and capability of the Soviet submarine fleets. The USA also has a large fleet of submarines, the major difference being that the USA has pursued a policy of building nuclear-powered submarines for all roles and has only a few diesel/electric boats. The United Kingdom has a mixed fleet, comprising nuclear powered, ballistic missile firers; nuclear hunter/killers; and diesel/electric hunter/killers. The French also possess the same mixed force of boats, but most other nations have only conventionally armed, diesel/electric boats in their fleets. The attraction of the submarine as a lethal, stealthy weapon system is very strong, and having looked closely at the Soviet fleets and given a passing mention of those of the Western navies, we should now concentrate on the methods of countering those submarines, of denying to the enemy the effective use of his submarines; in short, of conducting anti-submarine warfare.

DETECTION

The first stage in the often long process of achieving a kill against a submarine is detection. Detecting the presence of a submarine provides the impetus for further action and naturally narrows down the search area. Detection may be aided or even stimulated by intelligence on submarine movements, as was illustrated in the Second World War, but such intelligence may be good enough only to provide a general clue as to which area of water to search. Once the area has been defined as a sort of preliminary to the main action, the first step, that of actual detection, must be implemented. But submarines are now capable of spending a large proportion of their time at sea actually submerged. The art of searching underwater is still a confined business: light fades quickly and objects cannot be seen. Radar is nearly useless since radar waves do not penetrate water. However, the method of detection which was pursued and developed during the Second World War has remained as the principal means today, that of acoustic detection.

Acoustic Detection

Acoustic detection relies on the fact that sound travels far and relatively fast under water, and sensors, known as hydrophones, can pick up noises from sources up to several hundred miles away. The sound is energy in the form of pressure variations, known as sound waves, and in water these waves travel at speeds of between 4,700 and 5,100 feet per second. However, compared to, say, radar waves in the atmosphere travelling at 1,000 million feet per second, sound travels slowly enough to imply lengthy data acquisition and reaction times. Furthermore, refraction and attenuation of the sonar signal reduce the usable range quite significantly. The velocity of sound in water depends on the temperature, pressure and salinity of the water and increases as these factors increase.

As the variations in these factors are rarely constant and often unpredictable, the

PLATE 2.1. Submarine masts. (© *British Crown Copyright 1991/MOD*)

velocity of the sound wave may be correspondingly unpredictable. What makes this point so important is the corresponding fact that, as the velocity of the wave changes, so does the direction of travel. This change of direction, or bending of the ray, is considerable and cannot be ignored. The bending is comparable to the refraction of light, and the ray will bend from water which allows a high velocity towards water which allows a lower velocity.

In assessing exactly what a particular column of water will do to a sound wave passing through it, the effects of salinity are usually considered to be so small as to be ignored.

Combining the effect of the two remaining factors—temperature and pressure— results in a body of sea water having three discernible layers. The layer immediately below the surface is known as the *isothermal layer* as the temperature of the water in it is substantially constant because of the mixing of the water due to convection. In the South China Seas this layer may be only a few tens of feet deep, whereas in the North Atlantic it usually extends to a few hundred feet. Sound velocity in the isothermal layer increases slightly with depth, as the pressure is increasing slightly. Below the isothermal layer, the temperature of the water falls uniformly with depth until it reaches a steady, lower value at several thousand feet. This second layer is known as the *thermocline* and in it the effect of the decrease in temperature is greater than the effect of the increase in pressure. The velocity of sound waves therefore decreases with depth. And finally, beneath the thermocline there is the layer where temperature reaches a constant value, so that the only variation with depth is an increase in pressure. Since the velocity of sound waves increases with pressure, the velocity will now increase with depth in this part of the ocean, which is known as the *deep layer* (see Figure 2.1).

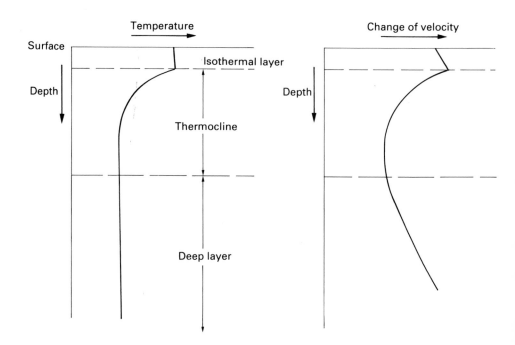

Fɪɢ. 2.1. How temperature and the velocity of sound waves vary with depth.

Other Sound Sources

In considering the effects of temperature and pressure on sound waves, the source of the sound has been assessed to be a submarine, the very system which is to be the object of attention for the anti-submarine forces. However, by no means all sound in the sea comes from submarines. The sources of noise which could affect a sonar receiver include breaking waves, various forms of marine life and, if close enough, other sonar equipment. One source of noise which affects ships or submarines operating sonar is their own radiated noise, or other self-noise which is detected by the hydrophones. Aircraft deploying sonobuoys into the water do not tend to generate self-noise in the same way. The sonobuoys will not often detect the aircraft's sound being transmitted through the air and then penetrating the ocean.

Passive and Active Acoustics

At this stage, it is appropriate to specify the two basic ways of using sound to detect submarines. The first is passive, that is, deploying hydrophones in sonobuoys from aircraft or in towed arrays from ships and submarines and merely listening. The distinct advantage of passive detection is that it does not alert the target to the presence of a hunter but, on the other hand, it does imply that the target is making sufficient noise to be heard above the ambient noise in the water. The second basic way of using sound is active, transmitting a pulse of sound energy and then listening for an echo. Although this method does allow detection of quiet targets, it alerts those targets to the presence of the hunter (see Figure 2.2).

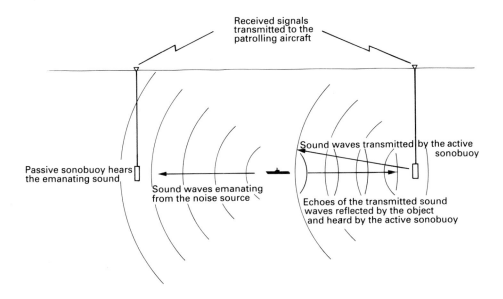

Received signals transmitted to the patrolling aircraft

Sound waves transmitted by the active sonobuoy

Passive sonobuoy hears the emanating sound

Sound waves emanating from the noise source

Echoes of the transmitted sound waves reflected by the object and heard by the active sonobuoy

Fig. 2.2. Passive and active sonar theory.

Sound Waves under Water

Adding to the complicated picture of the behaviour of sound waves under water, sound from, say, an active sonobuoy will travel in different ways in the several layers of water described earlier. In the isothermal layer, just below the surface, sound waves will be bent towards the surface and, on striking the surface, will be reflected down again until they once more bend upwards. The waves behave like this moving ever outward from the source until they finally run out of energy, that energy being absorbed by the water and the marine life in it. These particular waves are caught in the isothermal layer but effectively fill it, creating what is known as the *surface duct*.

Where the sound wave meets the boundary between the isothermal layer and the thermocline, the wave actually splits in two. One half is bent back upwards to remain in the surface duct as just described and the other enters the thermocline where it is immediately bent downwards in the 'slower' water. Between these two components of the sound wave there is nothing at all, no outward moving wave and therefore no returning echo. Any object in this zone would effectively be shadowed from the sound source and this area is therefore known as the shadow zone (see Figure 2.3).

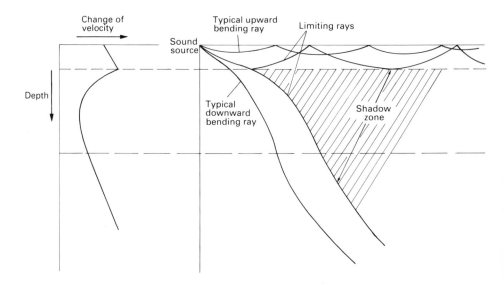

FIG. 2.3. The shadow zone.

Thus the thermocline is a formidable barrier in the detection of targets beneath the isothermal layer other than at very close range. The barrier is even more restricting in the tropics, where the isothermal layer is often shallow and where beneath it there is a much steeper temperature gradient than in temperate waters. One way in which this barrier might be overcome is in selecting specific cable lengths for the deployment of sonobuoys. Essentially the cable length is the depth at which the hydrophone system will hang from the flotation mechanism at the surface. A submarine may be in the shadow zone to a surface sonar system but will be detected by a hydrophone suspended into the thermocline.

Another phenomenon confusing the already complicated problem of collecting information from sound waves is that of *convergence zones*. When a sound wave, which has passed through the isothermal layer and into the thermocline, reaches the deep layer, it will be subjected to increasing pressure. This pressure will bend the wave upwards again and will also focus the wave causing it to converge. On striking the surface, the wave will be reflected again, first downwards to the deep layer then back up to the surface. The areas where the waves strike the surface are known as convergence zones and they are usually found as concentric circles around the source of the sound. In terms of distance they occur at about 30 nautical miles from the source then again at 60 nautical miles range (see Figure 2.4).

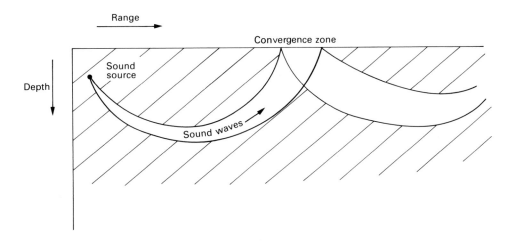

FIG. 2.4. Convergence zones.

While these observations on the behaviour of sound waves in water may have provided a diffuse picture, they are nevertheless only a basic summary of what is a complex subject. It is vitally necessary that the operators of the anti-submarine warfare aircraft and sensors know a great deal about the behaviour of sound waves under water. NATO operators are helped by organisations specifically created to provide bathythermal information, such as forecast temperature profile, forecast wind, wave height, gradient in the thermocline and ambient noise estimates for any given sea area. To bring such forecasts up to date, there are also bathythermal buoys (known as bathybuoys) which are buoys dropped into the water to sink at a known rate and provide a measurement of temperature at increasing depth. The information is processed and is presented to the operator as a velocity profile to be used in the calculation of expected ranges of detection on sonar buoys. Typically, an ASW aircraft on a task in a given area will drop at least one bathy buoy to bring up to date the information available on water conditions in that area.

The Doppler Effect   One more feature met with in the detection of sound waves from objects in the water actually works in favour of those attempting the detection. It is a feature encountered in several areas of technology and is not confined to sound waves in the sea. However, it is in the sea that it provides a source of information invaluable in the science and technology of submarine detection and location. The quality which adds so much to the picture is the Doppler effect. In simple terms, this is the phenomenon whereby the frequency of sound is altered by the movement of the sound source. A common illustration is that of standing on a railway station platform and listening to the whistle of an approaching train. As the train passes through the station the note of the whistle drops. The frequency of the note is increased when the source is approaching and decreased when it is receding.

Doppler under Water   Thus with sound waves underwater, some sonobuoys will report the frequency of the sound detected, and one of the variations in that frequency pattern will be due to the speed of the sound source relative to the buoy. Clearly, the variations due to Doppler will be greatest on any buoy directly in the path of the submarine: as the submarine moves straight towards the buoy there will be a maximum addition to the basic frequency because of the Doppler effect. As the submarine passes abeam the buoy, the effect of Doppler will be zero and the frequency detected will be the basic frequency of the engine noise. Then as the submarine sails directly away from the buoy, the detected noise will be the basic frequency with the maximum difference subtracted because of Doppler.

The effects of Doppler are predictable and regular and conform to simple rules; thus the position of a sound source relative to several buoys may be deduced from the rate of change of the Doppler frequencies. If the frequency remains high then suddenly drops through the basic frequency to a minimum as far below the basic value as the first was above it, then the submarine is very close to the buoy. If, on the other hand, the frequency slowly falls then the submarine is passing the buoy at some distance.

Unfortunately, of course, while these illustrations may be simple they do cover only the case in which a submarine is maintaining a steady course. Submarines rarely travel in straight lines, particularly when there is a suspicion that they may be being hunted. A change in frequency detected by a sonobuoy could therefore imply several things: a constant course at some distance, a changing course, or a changing speed.

Sonar on Ships and Aircraft

Across the range of systems engaged in anti-submarine warfare the common thread linking them all is the use of sound or sonar. Indeed, it is important that there are many varied systems available for no one system can encompass all the facilities required for pursuing a submarine from its initial detection to the final kill with a weapon in the water. While ships and submarines may be large enough to carry comprehensive and sensitive detection equipment and processing computers, they cannot with speed and precision switch search areas to move from one target to another. They also take a finite time to deploy to any given search area in the first instance.

Aircraft, on the other hand, can deploy rapidly either to an initial search area or between two search areas if required. Although aircraft cannot match the carrying capacity of ships or submarines, miniaturisation is making such progress that even aircraft can carry effective and comprehensive processing equipment to allow rapid interpretation of information from sonobuoys. Leaving these comparisons aside, neither submarines, nor ships nor aircraft can yet start from nothing in an open ocean and effectively conduct a successful search. Some initial clue is required to direct those assets to a more closely defined search area. That clue can be provided by intelligence, such as messages on the time of departure of submarines from their bases. But such intelligence is limited, for the submarine may submerge soon after departure and any clue as to its course and speed is then lost to the casual observer—except for sonar observations. It is again sonar on which the detection now depends.

Static Hydrophone Systems If in the First and the Second World Wars, stationary, moored hydrophones could be installed around coasts to detect the approach of enemy submarines, it is only a reasonable conceptual step to develop that principle and put static, moored hydrophones on the ocean floor in any part of the world where submarine activity would be of particular interest. This step is made all the more reasonable when geography plays a positive part, as it does in the relationship between the Soviet submarine bases in the Kola Peninsula, the transit areas down the north Norwegian Sea and the operating areas for some submarines, the north Atlantic. The seas off the coast of Norway are themselves relatively narrow when compared with the open Atlantic Ocean. Furthermore, submarines moving south-westerly from Kola to the north Atlantic must pass through one of the several so-called 'choke points' on their way. The relative positions of Greenland, Iceland, the Faroes and the United Kingdom all create choke points between them in which anti-submarine forces might be deployed to achieve the maximum effect with minimum effort.

Although the reasonable conceptual step mentioned earlier needed much technological innovation before being realised, the placing of sensitive hydrophones on the ocean floor in a pattern to detect transitting submarines has been achieved by the USA. Long-range passive acoustic detection with a sound surveillance system known as SOSUS has been in existence for some years. Information from SOSUS is used in directing aircraft, ships and submarines to specific areas to begin their own detailed search for potentially hostile submarines.

Towed-Array Systems In any sort of loose grading of sonar systems, in terms of range of detection, after SOSUS would come the towed-array systems now deployed on many frigates and submarines. While maritime air operations are primarily concerned with aircraft and their systems, a mention of towed array is necessary because it forms part of the integrated picture-gathering sequence which ultimately benefits all anti-submarine participants, including the aircraft.

Although there are some active towed-array sonars, the majority are passive and have an enormous range of detection. The ship or submarine self-noise does not reach them and they are themselves relatively easy to build. The ship or submarine platform generally has the capacity and power necessary to afford comprehensive processing equipment for the detected signals and there is virtually no limitation on the frequency of signals. One example of a passive towed array is the Plessey Compact Towed Array Sonar System and a diagram appears as Figure 2.5.

One active system is the *Active Towed Array System* (ATAS) a small, light-weight, high-performance sonar which uses a high-power, low-frequency trans-mitter deployed up to 1,000 yards behind the towing vessel. There is an in-line receiver array towed a further 330 yards behind the transmitter and the whole system can operate down to depths of 600 feet. The receiver array is 60 feet long and comprises mainly hydrophones and electronic systems. It can provide all-round cover, but at 90 degrees to the receiver the system achieves the best resolution, accurate to 0.5 of a degree.

Armed with information from either SOSUS or a towed-array system or both, an aircraft is then in a better position to confine its search area to a reasonable size. This advantage highlights the benefit of integrated anti-submarine warfare oper-ations, that is, the combining of all resources to capitalise on individual strengths and fill any gaps created by specific weaknesses.

Sonobuoys   The aircraft uses sonobuoys as its ears in the water and these are simply hydrophones suspended from a flotation device in the sea. The sound information detected by the buoy is transmitted to the receiver aircraft by radio and is processed on board that aircraft. Naturally, buoys dropped from aircraft are restricted in their detection ranges because of their small size. Furthermore, aircraft themselves are somewhat limited in the amount of processing equipment they can carry to make use of the information received. Nevertheless, the sonobuoy does give the aircraft a capability it would not otherwise have. On entering an area in which the presence of a submarine is suspected, an aircraft would drop several buoys in a pattern to detect the source of the sound and to classify it as a submarine. This is the next significant step in the inexorable process of anti-submarine warfare.

Once convinced that the contact is a submarine, the crew may even identify a particular submarine type by its sound signatures in terms of whether it is powered by nuclear or diesel/electric propulsion; whether it is Soviet, American, British or other nationality; and whether it is a particular boat in one of those general classes.

Localisation   After detection and classification of the target, the next step is to find it precisely or, in the accepted term, 'localise' it. Localisation is achieved by using more patterns of buoys, either repeats of the initial pattern or other, distinctive, patterns, as dictated by the scenario. For example, if in a line of buoys a crew could discern that the submarine was close to one particular buoy, they could drop a circle of buoys around that buoy. On the other hand, if in the process of detection and classification the crew had also gleaned information on the submar-ine's course and speed, they could drop a pattern of buoys ahead of the calculated position of the target to determine its precise position. Generally the closer a submarine sails to a buoy, the more information that buoy can provide and the more accurate the information will be.

Tracking   Once the submarine has been localised then precise tracking is required so that the aircraft can attack. The weapons that an aircraft carries for

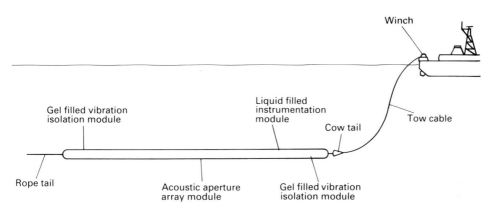

Fɪɢ. 2.5. Plessey Compact Towed Array System.

anti-submarine warfare generally takes time to deploy, and thus an attack is always aimed at a position to which a submarine will sail, rather than a position where it was known to have been. Precise tracking requires information on the course and speed of the submarine and these may be deduced from the information gleaned from the sonar buoys. While computerised processing equipment is vital to ensure accurate and speedy deductions, operators may also use the raw information provided and make their own assessments of where the submarine is and what course and speed he is making.

Both in localisation and tracking the sonobuoy information is continually assessed, whether it be a bearing, a range and bearing from an active buoy, or a Doppler frequency or any combination of all of them. However, only in tracking is the aim to be so precise and to predict the future movement so accurately as to facilitate an attack with an underwater weapon. Active sonobuoys provide more rapid and usable information from single buoys for tracking, but they do suffer from the disadvantage of alerting the target. A number of passive buoys, on the other hand, will provide information of equal quality as bearings from each buoy to the submarine. It requires just a little more time to assess these bearings and to decide that where they intersect is the submarine's present position; but is not thereby alerted. Whatever the source of tracking information, as soon as the crew are convinced they can predict with some assurance where the submarine is going next, they can press home their attack with their special-to-type weapons.

Non-Acoustic Detection

Undoubtedly, acoustics make a great contribution to the detection, classification, localisation, tracking and finally the killing of submarines. However, there are other means of detection which either complement or confirm acoustic information. For instance, during the Second World War, visual searches for submarines were commonly the means of detection. Despite the great development in submarine technology and their operations and despite the ability of submarines to remain submerged for much longer periods, there are even today frequent visual cues on the surface to betray the presence of a submarine.

A nuclear submarine will come close enough to the surface to extend its masts above the water, perhaps to locate an enemy, to communicate with its own forces, or to fix its position. In a reasonably smooth sea, a collection of masts above the water will create a tell-tale wake which is visible from an aircraft up to several miles away. A diesel/electric submarine either moving under the power of diesel engines or using the engines to recharge the batteries will put the snorting mast above the surface. Thus there are opportunities, however slim, when an alert aircraft crew could visually detect the masts of a submerged submarine. One development after the Second World War was Autolycus, a system designed to 'sniff' the exhaust fumes from the diesel engines of a submarine. However, this did not prove generally successful and other non-acoustic measures have achieved more prominence.

Radar   The lesson from the Second World War is that visual detection ranges are usually low, but, in conditions of bad weather or darkness, visual detection is impossible. It was this factor which drove the Allies to develop an airborne radar capable of detecting enemy submarines on the surface. Airborne radars have now developed so much that they can detect the masts of a submerged submarine at ranges of more than 10 miles.

Electronic Support Measures (ESM)   Should a submarine foolishly push a mast above the surface to communicate, the submarine's own transmissions may be detected by an aircraft using electronic support equipment. The crew can then estimate the submarine's position from the bearing and strength of the transmission. Identifying the particular type of transmission may also help in deciding the class of submarine.

Magnetic Anomaly Detector   One device which, in the Second World War, was extremely reliable in registering the presence of a submarine, albeit from very short range, was the magnetic anomaly detector (MAD). MAD was the system which detected the presence of a ferrous object by registering a disturbance in the earth's magnetic field. While certain progress has been made on the reliability and operation of MAD systems since then, they remain essentially short-range systems. The significance of the short range is that an aircraft has to fly directly over the submarine before there is a 'MAD mark'. This factor cuts both ways: on the one hand, it seems that MAD is no use for initial search and detection. However, on the other, it means that after localisation and tracking, if a MAD mark is obtained it is a virtual guarantee that at that moment the aircraft is over the submarine.

THE KILL

Having used non-acoustic as well as the acoustic methods of detecting and tracking submarines, the ASW crew is now ready to drop a weapon to kill the submarine. The aim is to put an explosive charge close enough to it to inflict lethal damage, and this usually means puncturing the pressure hull. Either a relatively small charge is used to explode right against the hull or a much bigger one may be employed to allow for some error in placing the charge. The ultimate example is the nuclear depth bomb in service with several anti-submarine forces. The strength of the blast compensates for a relatively large aiming error, because the explosion of the bomb will inflict damage on the submarine even from a considerable distance. However, the use of nuclear weapons could be severely constrained by political considerations. Consequently, there remains a continuing need to develop non-nuclear alternatives.

Other depth bombs with much smaller explosive charges would need to explode much nearer the target to achieve a comparable effect, and, to help eliminate as much aiming error as possible, several depth bombs would be dropped at a time in a stick. This method was used extensively in the Second World War, and with variations in the stick spacing and in the depth settings of the bombs, results could be adjusted and dramatically improved. But even sticks of depth bombs rely on the aircraft's dropping them as close as possible to a predicted position of the target. The logic also depends on the predicted position being accurate, or on the fact that the submarine will maintain the course and speed which determined the predicted position. If the submarine changes course and speed, the predicted position will be incorrect and the bombs will not explode close enough to inflict the necessary amount of damage.

The Torpedo

Far more preferable is the system which, though needing to be dropped accurately, will itself detect the submarine and home towards it, with a detonation as the weapon strikes the submarine. The torpedo uses acoustics to detect and then home on to the submarine, and is completely independent after leaving the aircraft. The drawbacks are that the torpedo has to be a lightweight version to permit its carriage by aircraft, and this naturally reduces the size and therefore the lethality of the warhead. Against a thick or even a double-hulled submarine, a lightweight torpedo warhead may not be effective because of lack of penetration. Clearly the need is paramount for anti-submarine aircraft crews to work hard at their assessments of where the submarine is, of where it is going and of where their weapon release point should be to give their torpedo as much chance of success as possible.

3

Anti-Submarine Warfare Aircraft

Conducting anti-submarine warfare involves painstakingly collecting items of information from various sources and putting them together to create an assessment of where a submarine might be. In airborne ASW, the sensors for collecting target information and the weapons to kill the submarine all need to be carried in an aircraft. The attributes of an anti-submarine warfare aircraft are dictated by the requirements of the task. In broad terms, the aircraft should be able to detect, classify, locate, track and attack submarines, and it will therefore need a suite of detection systems and a selection of weapons.

DETECTION SYSTEMS

Beginning with visual detection, the aircraft should have good look-out positions, including clear-view pilots' cockpits and bubble windows for beam observation posts. The aircraft should have a modern air-to-surface radar capable of detecting not only submarines on the surface but also the masts protruding above the surface when a submarine is at periscope depth. For passive detection an aircraft will need a comprehensive ESM system for receiving, identifying and estimating the position of transmissions by the submarine, be they communications or radar transmissions.

Since submerged submarines can still best be detected by acoustic systems, the aircraft should carry enough sonobuoys of the appropriate types to ensure successful detection in a mixture of scenarios. Information from those buoys needs comprehensive processing to translate raw sound reception into sifted information which will assist in building the picture of where the submarine might be. Thus computerised processors are vital. Once an aircraft crew are reasonably sure they are tracking a submarine by the use of acoustics, they need to have precise and reasonably high-confidence position-information before pressing home an attack. While acoustics can be refined to give such confidence, a confirmatory signal from an independent source is highly desirable. A magnetic anomaly detection system will provide such information, and it is essential that the ideal anti-submarine warfare aircraft has a MAD system.

NAVIGATION AND COMMUNICATION SYSTEMS

Since the aircraft will be operating over large tracts of open ocean, it will require high precision navigation systems such as very low frequency (VLF) *Omega*, an inertial platform, Doppler radar and Loran. It will also require long-range communications equipment, such as high frequency (HF) or satellite communications links. Submarine patrol areas and other likely areas where submarines might attack merchant shipping or naval units are usually some considerable distance from land, thus requiring long-range performance from the aircraft. Not only that, but to compile a submarine plot using the available sensors does take time and thus the aircraft will need to be able to loiter in the patrol area once it has arrived there, extending the requirement for range and endurance yet further.

CREW REQUIREMENTS

Clearly, flying such long-range sorties with such a complex task will be demanding on the crew, so that one important requirement is that the aircraft should be large enough to permit some considerations of crew comfort, such as sound proofing, comfortable seats, space and a galley for hot food. All of these requirements dictate a large, economical aircraft, and several nations have opted for their MPA to be derivatives of reliable, long-range airliners. This approach has proved to be very successful and there are several aircraft types which illustrate the point.

THE NIMROD MR Mk 2

The *Nimrod* MR Mk 2 aircraft, in service as the long-range MPA of the Royal Air Force, is based on the *Comet* airliner design. It has four Roll-Royce *Spey* engines and an enlarged fuselage to accommodate a weapons bay as well as a radar scanner in the nose. Because the view from the pilot's cockpit was limited, extra windows were added for better look-out. But there remain windows down the side of the fuselage, including one bubble window on each side for the beam look-outs and one for the air electronics officer.

PLATE 3.1. *Nimrod*. (*British Aerospace*)

The Crew

The *Nimrod* has an operational crew of about 14, depending on the mission, and the airframe is large enough to accommodate these men quite comfortably. While the two pilots are ably assisted by the flight engineer in performing such evolutions as closing down two of the four engines for fuel economy at low level, the two navigators concentrate on the tactical aspects. An air electronics officer supervises the communications expert and the sensor team, which comprises the 'dry' men (those operating the *Searchwater* radar and the *Yellowgate* ESM equipment) and the 'wet' men (those attending to the acoustics, buoys as well as processors).

Engine

The *Nimrod* is the only long-range MPA in the world to employ jet propulsion, as all the other such aircraft are turboprop types. Jet propulsion gives the *Nimrod* a distinct advantage in a high transit speed, enabling it to react quickly when tasked to fly to a suspected submarine position. Although this means that the fuel consumption is correspondingly high, one way to reduce the effect of that penalty is to fly the patrol part of the sortie on only two engines instead of four. Thus it is standard practice for *Nimrod* crews to close down two of their engines once they are established on task and below a critical weight. Obviously the critical weight is determined as the weight below which the aircraft could still climb away to a safe level to relight the shut-down engines if one of the two operating engines were to suffer some sort of failure.

Performance

The changes to the *Comet* airframe already mentioned were taken further with the addition of a MAD aerial in a tail boom to keep the aerial as far away as possible from the metallic mass of the aircraft. Larger intake areas were also required for the *Spey* engines, with the inboard intakes needing a 21% increase and the outboards one of 15%. A six-feet long plug was taken out of the fuselage just ahead of the wing to improve the directional stability, but the final result of this move was doubtful. A searchlight was fitted into the starboard external wing tank in such a way as to be controllable from the cockpit. The undercarriage was strengthened all round to cope with the increased all-up weight of the *Nimrod* over the *Comet*. The performance figures which emerged for the *Nimrod* included a maximum speed of 500 kts, a patrol speed of 300 kts, with a range of 5,000 n miles and a patrol endurance of nine hours. The service ceiling is 42,000 feet and the weapons bay can carry up to nine *Stingray* or Mk 46 torpedoes, or a mixture of torpedoes and depth bombs. In the rescue configuration, the weapons bay can accommodate several variations of rescue gear, including dinghies and containers of survival equipment.

Improvements   The upgrade from MR1 to MR2 *Nimrod* meant very little change to the airframe. The installation of the *Searchwater* radar to replace the ASV21 and the improvements to the avionics and central tactical system (CTS) were all internal modifications which enhanced the capability of the aircraft enormously without affecting the frame itself. The changes which did affect the airframe were stimulated by the *Nimrod*'s participation in the Falklands War of 1982. The range of the *Nimrod* needed to be extended dramatically and air-to-air refuelling was the answer. Although an air-to-air refuelling capability for *Nimrod* had been discussed several times earlier, this facility had never been fitted to the fleet. However, very quickly some ex-*Vulcan* probes and much bowser hosing were fitted to the *Nimrod* and worked extremely well.

The capability was so impressive that after the war the modifications to the aircraft were upgraded and made of a more permanent and aesthetic nature: the large diameter bowser hose did not survive to snake its way along the cabin floor but was properly routed and housed under the floor. The effect of the probes on the directional stability of the aircraft needed to be offset and the solution was to fit a small ventral fin as well as finlets on the tailplane.

The other external change was the addition of pylons to the underwing for carrying and firing the *Sidewinder* AIM9 air-to-air missile. The air-to-air missile subsequently fitted to *Nimrod* was the *Harpoon*, two of which can now be carried in the weapons bay.

Searchwater Radar   One of the most significant improvements in the update of the *Nimrod* from MR1 to MR2 standard was the installation of the *Searchwater* radar. This Thorn-EMI Electronics system is controlled by a Ferranti 1600D digital computer, to offer multiple-target tracking and a classification capability, permitting the study of the outlines of targets at long ranges. Specifically designed for the maritime role, the radar gives high detection and tracking performance despite high sea states. To aid classification the system incorporates Identification Friend or Foe (IFF) and also contains an air-to-air and a weather mode. Targets of interest and their associated data can be passed direct to the central tactical system.

Although the precise details of the performance of *Searchwater* remains classified, the system was introduced to replace the old ASV21 radar as fitted to the MR1. The ASV21 could detect large ships out to 150 nautical miles, vessels under 100 tons at 40 n miles, surfaced submarines at 75 n miles and snorting submarines at 20 n miles. The *Searchwater* should be capable of achieving ranges greater than these and has the two distinct advantages of, first, being able to provide a visual reproduction of the radar profile of the target ship and, secondly, being able to pass relevant information to the CTS for rapid interpretation by the tactical navigator.

The detection of small targets in high sea states is improved by using frequency agility as well as the addition of the digital computer for signal processing. The operator is presented with a bright, flicker-free picture by a digital integrating scan-converter which also makes a simple co-ordination of both target and transponder returns.

Loral 1017A: Yellowgate   Another relatively new aid to detection and location of either submarines or surface ships is the Loral 1017A ESM equipment known as *Yellowgate*. The system has an extremely wide Radio Frequency (RF) bandwidth, works on the agile supernet principle and is controlled by a GEC-

Marconi 920 ATC and a Texas Instrument 2520 digital computer. It gives the crew information based on intercepted transmissions, and includes warning, classification and direction-finding facilities. The classification procedure is based on comparisons of the features of the intercepted signal with a computer memory store of many of the transmissions likely to be heard. Again, a distinct advantage of this new system is that relevant and verified information may be passed from the ESM position directly to the tactical navigator's CTS.

Much of the ESM equipment is housed within the aircraft and the aerials are in two wingtip pods, now a good visual feature of the *Nimrod* MR2. While the emission-control policy of many navies is making effective progress and severely restricting the electronic transmissions made by individual units, there are many occasions when transmissions of some sort have to be made. Examples include vital communications, occasional sweeps of area-defence radars, and the concentrated aiming of live-fire-control radars. All of these transmissions, for however short a period, can be detected by systems such as *Yellowgate*. They may then be compared, identified and given a bearing, so assisting in the search for a particular target or, at the very least, helping in building up a picture of the positions of several units.

Magnetic Anomaly Detector   Another sensor which provides information on the possible presence of submarines is the MAD system. Clearly, the hope is that any register on this instrument while it is out over the ocean indicates the metal mass of a submarine underneath the airframe. The MAD system quite recently fitted to the *Nimrod* MR2 is the Advanced Integrated MAD system or AIMS, ASQ-504(v) built by CAE Electronics. There are several phenomena which will cause the AIMS to register an anomaly and the *Nimrod* crew attempt to keep the instances of these as restricted as possible in order to isolate the real signalling of the presence of a submarine.

The standard practice is also to fly a set pattern of heading, pitch and roll manoeuvres so that the system operator may, via a computer, measure then apply a set of compensations to offset the effects of the aircraft's mass and manoeuvres. The system can also detect submarines, despite the presence of 'noise'. The sudden movement of the AIMS pen across the tracing paper indicating a likely submarine spurs the operator to press an event marker which ensures that the position of the aircraft at that time is displayed on the central tactical system display screen.

Sonobuoys

The *Nimrod* carries a range of sonobuoys and will use all or selected types depending on the scenario. A LOFAR buoy provides *Low-Frequency Analysis and Recording* of the discrete frequencies emanating from a submarine and makes possible their display within the aircraft. The current design of the SSQ 904 LOFAR buoy has evolved over several years and is widely used by MPA as it measures only 12 inches long and weighs only 10 lbs. This size is known as an 'F' size and may be carried in large numbers in the *Nimrod*. It is an omnidirectional, passive sonobuoy which has a choice of up to 99 RF channels and a choice of three operating periods, of one, three or eight hours. It also has a selectable hydrophone depth.

DIFAR Buoy   Targets may be localised by omnidirectional buoys, but the process may take a considerable time. This time may be reduced by employing a more complex passive buoy known as the *Directional Frequency Analysis and Recording* type or DIFAR buoy. This type of DIFAR used by the *Nimrod* is the SSQ 954A, a 'G'-size buoy being 16.5 inches long and weighing 15 lbs. It has autonomous function selection, in that any required frequency can be set for the fully-synthesised Very High Frequency (VHF) transmitter; and the operating period and the hydrophone depth are also programmable. The operating period may be one, three or eight hours and the depth may be 30, 100 or 300 m. On deployment from the aircraft, a plate falls away from the device, allowing a parachute to deploy and slow the velocity to 30 metres per second. As the buoy enters the water, the cross chute is released and water enters the housing thus energising a sea water battery. A carbon dioxide cylinder is ruptured inflating a float bag to erect an integral antenna. The housing and termination assembly descend to the preselected depth, whereupon the housing separates from the directional hydrophone assembly and the buoy begins to operate. The directional hydrophone provides sine and cosine signals which are then multi-plexed with the omnidirectional hydrophone and the compass signal. This complex signal is then used to modulate the VHF transmitter in the surface unit. A diagram of the suspension and deployment sequence of the SSQ 954A DIFAR buoy is at Figure 3.1.

BARRA Buoy   The Beamed Array Analysis (BARRA) buoy, or SSQ 801, is an Australian-designed passive buoy which can give extremely accurate bearings of noise sources. An 'A' size buoy, three feet long, it has five 'arms' which deploy like an umbrella fame. Each arm carries five hydrophones. The life of the buoy may be selected from a list of available times, and there is also a choice of shallow or medium depth and a variety of RF channels available.

Bathythermal buoy   The bathythermal buoy carried by the *Nimrod* is the type SSQ 937 which is an 'F'-size buoy preset to one of three standard RF channels. Once in the water it operates continuously from the surface to a minimum depth of 1,000 feet, measuring water temperature to an accuracy of $\pm 1°C$. It descends in the water at about five feet per second and its operating life is approximately five minutes.

Ranger Buoy   Establishing the range of a submarine using an active buoy is accomplished with the *Ranger* or SSQ 47B buoy. This is an 'A'-size buoy, three feet long and almost five inches in diameter. It can be operated effectively from ranges up to 10 nautical miles at altitudes of 500 to 10,000 feet and in sea conditions of up to sea state five. A series of separate VHF channels permits interference-free operation of up to six sonobuoys either individually or simultaneously in a single sonobuoy field. The significant features in this active, ranging buoy are the trans-ducer, the electronics components package, the single-unit submerged battery

PLATE 3.2. *Nimrod*—Sonobuoy racks. (*Dowty Maritime Systems Ltd*)

package, the high-pressure battery operation and the facility for very deep operation.

   CAMBS Buoy   Another 'A'-sized, active buoy is the CAMBS or Command, Active, Multibeam Sonobuoy. This buoy comes with a choice of 31 RF Channels, three selectable hydrophone depths and a one-hour operating life. The sonobuoy can be controlled by commands transmitted via a radio link from the aircraft. On deployment from the aircraft, a parachute slows down the rate of descent to about 30 metres per second. On hitting the sea, the parachute is automatically jettisoned and a combined float and antenna system is erected. Simultaneously, the sub-surface unit, which is attached to the surface unit by a signal suspension cable, descends to one of three preselectable depths. When the unit reaches the required depth, the sonobuoy begins to operate in the passive mode. In this mode, the buoy relays all signals detected by the receiver-array hydrophones, together with magnetic compass information, to the aircraft via the telemetry link.
   In the active mode, acoustic pulses are emitted from the omnidirectional projector and the returned echoes are detected by the receiver array. These echoes and relevant compass information are amplified and fed to a multiplexer where they are combined to provide a multiplexed signal. It is this signal which is transmitted to the aircraft, where it is processed to derive a fix of detected targets. A diagram of the deployment and suspension sequence of the SSQ 963A (CAMBS) is shown at Figure 3.2.

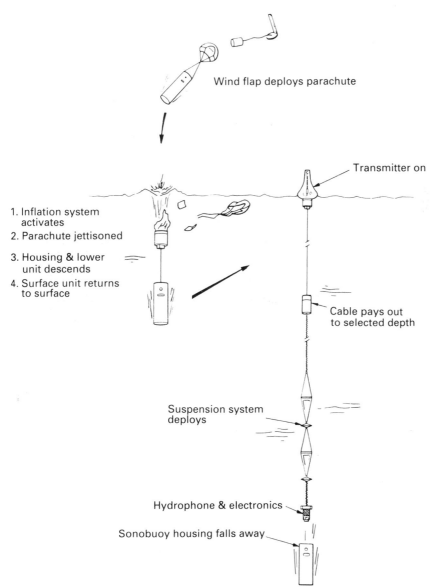

Wind flap deploys parachute

Transmitter on

1. Inflation system
   activates
2. Parachute jettisoned

3. Housing & lower
   unit descends

4. Surface unit returns
   to surface

Cable pays out
to selected depth

Suspension system
deploys

Hydrophone & electronics

Sonobuoy housing falls away

FIG. 3.1. DIFAR suspension and deployment.

Processors

Early attempts to use sonobuoys to locate submerged submarines relied on the hearing of the sound being picked up by each sonobuoy in turn and then deciding upon the boat's position on the basis of the comparative strength of the signals. As buoys developed, it quickly became clear that some sort of processing system was necessary to filter, clarify and interpret all of the information being received in the aircraft. Some processors were inflexible, as both the frequency band and the

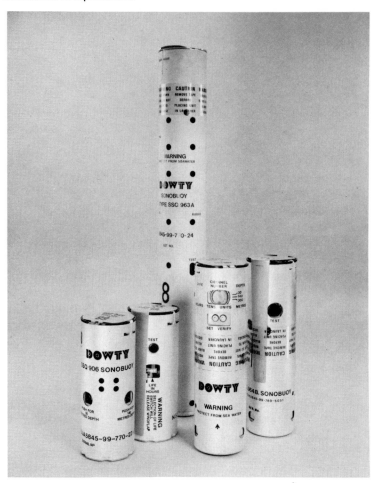

PLATE 3.3. Buoys. (*Dowty Maritime Systems Ltd*)

analysis resolution were limited in coverage. Furthermore, the processors could handle a maximum of only four buoys and their directional capability was slow and relatively inaccurate.

The AQS 901 Processor   A new processor for the *Nimrod* MR2 was designated AQS 901. It was specifically designed to meet the growing threat from faster, deeper and much quieter submarines. Computer-based, it permits maximum flexibility of processing and display of data from current and known future sonobuoys. The system incorporates a flexible display sub-system using cathode ray tubes (CRT) and multi-channel paper recorders which allow the operator to use the many processing modes built into the system. To control command-activated sonobuoys, AQS 901 has a command transmitter system, and the modern eight-channel receiver system operates on standard frequencies, allowing all current and planned future buoys to be processed.

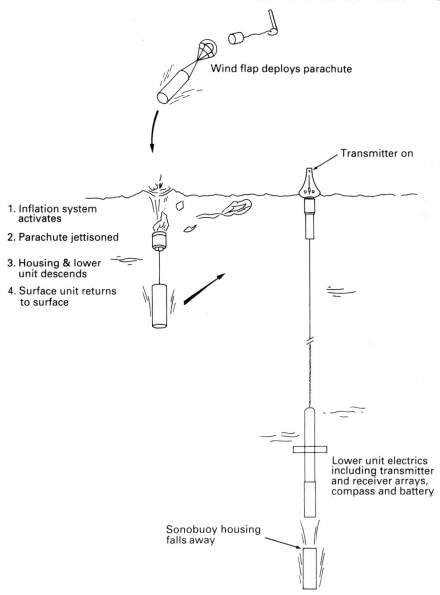

Wind flap deploys parachute

Transmitter on

1. Inflation system activates

2. Parachute jettisoned

3. Housing & lower unit descends

4. Surface unit returns to surface

Lower unit electrics including transmitter and receiver arrays, compass and battery

Sonobuoy housing falls away

FIG. 3.2. CAMBS suspension and deployment.

The system provides powerful broadband and vernier window facilities, together with the normal wideband frequency analysis. Some of the basic features of the system are: a powerful, high-speed 920 ATC computer to act as the system manager and central processor; separate bulk memory units to increase the memory capacity and data throughput rate; a microprogrammed fast Fourier transform analyser capable of performing a 2048 point complex transform in 11.26

PLATE 3.4. Buoys about to be loaded onto *Nimrod*. (*Dowty Maritime Systems Ltd*)

milliseconds; microprogrammed beamformers for array sonobuoys; and comprehensive hard copy and CRT display suites.

The *Nimrod* MR2 is fitted with two AQS 901 processing systems operating side
by side. The operators have two acoustic display units from each AQS 901, and a
tote display unit is available for a co-ordinator. The display performance has been
designed to present various display formats required by the flexible system.
Alongside the displays, the display and processor control panel forms part of the
facia at each control station. The basic facilities include a keyset, special button
actions and a rolling ball, all of which allow the operator to input his requests for
special processing modes, to indicate where and how the results are to be presented, to control the operation of any command-activated buoys deployed and to
interrogate any of the displays.

Data Handling   The aim of the processing system is to gather acoustic information from sonobuoys and then convert that into tactical inputs for the co-
ordinator. In the *Nimrod* the tactical navigator is the co-ordinator and he sits at a
console controlling, inputting and interrogating the CTS. The AQS 901 systems are
linked to the CTS via a serial data interface with suitable buffering. Data are
transferred as a series of messages and the update rates are dependent on the type

PLATE 3.5. Inside a *Nimrod*—Acoustics and Nav station. (*Dowty Maritime Systems Ltd*)

of message and the current processing being carried out. The sorts of message to be transferred include buoy number, contact identifier, bearing, associated bearing accuracy and data effectiveness time. There are also Doppler fixing data, including contact identification, position and velocity components as well as classifications by contact identifier and type.

In all, the two AQS 901 systems in the *Nimrod* comprise 46 units, including control panels and displays. At the time of its introduction, its makers were convinced that AQS 901 was the most complex, airborne, acoustic processing system built in Europe. It is proving to be a highly successful and reliable equipment.

The Central Tactical System

Having launched sonobuoys and received their signals and having had these signals processed through the AQS 901, the information beginning to accumulate on the target submarine is displayed to the tactical navigator on the screen of his CTS. The system is based on the Marconi 920 ATC digital computer and can handle inputs from radar, ESM, MAD and manual keying as well as the acoustics from the AQS 901. The computer continually calculates the aircraft's current position and this is displayed on the CTS screen together with any information from other sensors and sources.

The tactical navigator has control over what is displayed and, furthermore, is trained to accord grades of reliability to the information and therefore to the conclusions to which it leads him. Just because the information is displayed convincingly on a neat and tidy electronic screen it does not automatically mean that the information is reliable. However, the CTS does allow the rapid making of decisions to flow much more smoothly. Additionally the pictorial representation of the world outside the aircraft, including sonobuoys, surface contacts, ESM bearings, and possible target positions is extremely valuable. The pilots are involved in the distribution of CTS information, as the computer will provide them with steering information to specific points nominated by the navigators.

Navigation Systems

For navigation, the *Nimrod* has some excellent equipment which is specifically aimed at overcoming those problems of inaccuracies in positional information. The information is required not only in order to know where the aircraft is, but also, and probably more important, in order to tell other people where the enemy is, whether it be a ship or a submarine. The concept in the *Nimrod* is that all the navigation equipment can be used to drive the positional information of the CTS. The choice of which equipment provides which input can be controlled by the routine navigator, and can be selected automatically as various instruments and equipment are degraded.

The basic equipment for heading and initial position information is a Ferranti 1012 Inertial Navigation System. On initial alignment, this equipment may take either a stored heading (if the aircraft has not been moved since the previous shutdown) or the heading derived from the twin Sperry GM7 compasses. Once aligned and airborne, the system has a Decca Doppler input of drift and groundspeed. The Inertial Navigation System heading is the principal source of heading; but the most accurate position is most often that generated by the CTS and the Marconi 920 ATC computer. Should other components fail, the basic reversion is to a GM7 compass heading input, combined with the input from an air data computer.

Aircraft Position

A constant display of the aircraft's position is provided by a routine dynamic display, which projects light in the form of an aircraft symbol on to the chart attached to his table by the routine navigator. Other navigation aids at his disposal include a Litton *Omega*, a long-range navigation aid which operates in the VLF band. Additionally LORAN C is a pulsed hyperbolic navigation aid with accuracies of between one and five nautical miles in areas where there is good ground cover from fixed stations. The list of aids is almost completed by mentioning Auto Direction Finding (ADF) compasses, VOR/ILS and TACAN. Almost, but not quite complete, since the *Nimrod* does carry sextants and the necessary mounting for using them in observing the sun or stars to derive a position line from the observed angle above the horizon.

Radios

The *Nimrod* carries two HF radios for long-range communication with maritime HQ and other agencies. There is also a low-frequency, very-long-range receiver for the receipt of coded orders and radio airborne teletype messages. For secure and clear voice transmission and reception, the *Nimrod* has the *Nestor* 'scrambler' system, which is gradually being overtaken by the *Lamberton* system, which does the same thing but with a much larger choice of frequencies. Standard twin Ultra High Frequency (UHF)/VHF radio sets are also fitted and, finally, there is a VHF/Frequency Modulation (FM) Pye *Westminster* radio for direct communication with merchant shipping, larger pleasure craft and yachts, HM Coastguards and British Telecom radio stations.

Weapons

The *Nimrod* is armed with a mix of weapons, depending on the specific mission. Anti-submarine weapons are the major components in this list, but the aircraft can carry the *Harpoon* anti-ship missile in the bomb bay. The *Harpoon* and its capabilities will be discussed in the chapter on anti-surface unit warfare. Another specialist weapon is the AIM 9 (G or L) *Sidewinder* missile for self-defence and this weapon will be covered in the air defence section. The *Nimrod* also has the capability to carry and deliver American-made nuclear depth bombs, but more details of that system are classified.

The conventional anti-submarine weapons are therefore the torpedoes: the MK 46 and the *Stingray*. The MK 46 is a light-weight, deep-diving and high-speed torpedo, fitted with an acoustic homing system which can be either active or passive. After entering the water, the MK 46 searches for, acquires and then homes on to the target.

The Stingray Torpedo   A more modern torpedo, the *Stingray*, is nevertheless of a relatively conventional configuration (see Figure 3.3). The homing system is acoustic and the nose contains the sonar transducers, as well as all the transmitters, power electronics and receivers. In the guidance and control section, the processing electronics are located alongside the target-recognition facilities and the on-board computer. Being a totally computer-controlled weapon, the algorithms and software manage not only the acoustics and homing but also the torpedo guidance and tactics. For instance, the weapon selects the optimum tactic to attack the target and, if it misses, controls the subsequent re-attack. The propulsion system and control surfaces are naturally in the tail of the torpedo and the sea water activated battery is just forward, close to the centre of gravity. Right at the rear is a parachute to reduce water-entry speed and to slow the sink rate once the torpedo is in the water. The final part of the torpedo is the warhead and this, in the form of a shaped charge, is just behind the homing system.

Stingray is propelled by an electric motor driving two contra-rotating pulsors housed in a duct which form a pump jet. This system is not only compact, it is also very efficient and much quieter than conventional propeller drives. A major part of the design effort in the propulsion system was in seeking and identifying the optimum balance of speed and endurance. The small control surfaces are electro-

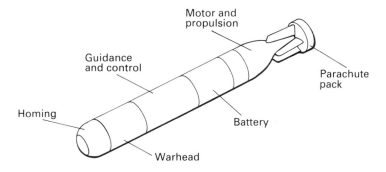

Motor and
propulsion

Guidance
and control

Parachute
pack

Homing

Battery

Warhead

Fɪɢ. 3.3. Cutaway of *Stingray* missile.

hydraulically controlled and are sited in the efflux from the pump jet. This arrangement enhances the performance of the control surfaces, ensuring that the turn rate
and agility of the *Stingray* are very good.

The power source itself is a magnesium/silver chloride battery with a sea-water
electrolyte. The battery is completely inert until water enters, when it has to fill
rapidly so that there is power available after a second and a half. The angle of water
entry is critical. If the angle is too shallow, the battery will not fill rapidly enough
and the tail-heavy torpedo may be pointing to the surface when power becomes
available. In this case it might drive itself out of the water. Conversely, if the water
entry angle is too steep, the torpedo may hit the bottom before it is brought under
control (see Figure 3.4).

a. Too shallow   b. Too steep

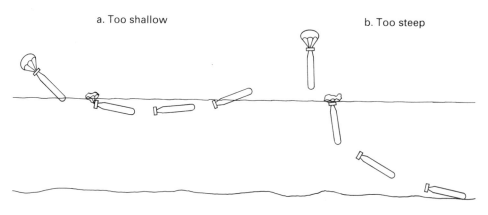

Fɪɢ. 3.4. *Stingray* missile water entry angles.

Once in the water and under control, the torpedo starts an acoustic search for the
target. *Stingray* has an advanced acoustic transmission system, yet the guaranteed
detection and classification range in active transmission is small when compared to
above-water systems. Naturally, the range is extended when the torpedo is engaged
in the purely listening mode, but, in that case, the ability to establish the distance to
the target is not available. The design of the torpedo incorporates the balance to be

struck between a sensitive and capable electro-acoustic transducer, and equipment small enough to fit into the nose of a torpedo and rugged enough to withstand the vibrations as the weapon moves through the water. Even the sound of the water flowing past the nose may mask the usually very small acoustic returns from targets. In *Stingray* the homing system uses the basic properties of sound in sea water to acquire and home on to the submarine target. By suitable switching, the electrically-activated transducers in the nose can transmit high-power sound then detect and receive the much lower power returns.

The modern digital computer in *Stingray* controls all the functions from propulsion to homing and decides on the required transmit and receive modes and attack tactics. The system is sensitive enough, through frequency-modulated transmission, to differentiate between real targets, the bottom of the ocean and even countermeasures deployed by potential targets. Another task of the computer is to control the depth of the torpedo: if the water is very shallow, the torpedo runs along a fixed-height contour, following the ocean floor. It then goes through a search pattern until the target is acquired. After initial approach homing, the torpedo measures the aspect and the speed of the target and then calculates the best course for it to come into collision with the target, having allowed for the terminal homing phase. In this phase, the torpedo turns in sharply so as to strike the target at right angles to the hull, at a position where the warhead will be most effective.

The *Stingray* has a shaped-charge or directed-energy warhead which produces a molten jet of copper to drill a hole through the pressure hull of a submarine, having first penetrated several metres of outer hull. Again, the advantage of the *Stingray*'s terminal homing phase plays a major part, as the shaped-charge warhead needs to be as close as possible to normal incidence to the hull to ensure penetration.

THE LOCKHEED P3C *ORION*

The long-range maritime patrol and anti-submarine warfare aircraft of the US Navy is the Lockheed P3C *Orion*. A development of the Lockheed *Electra* airliner, the *Orion* entered service in August 1962 and has undergone several modernisation programmes since then. Powered by four Allison T56 turboprop engines, the *Orion* has a mission radius of about 2,000 miles and a typical sortie would last about 12 hours. The main bases for P3C operations in the Atlantic are Naval Air Station (NAS) Brunswick and NAS Jacksonville, but units are regularly deployed to Keflavik, Lajes, Rota, Bermuda, Souda Bay and Sigonella. The P3C carries a crew of from 10 to 12 men, depending on the specific mission; the individual specialisations may include: three pilots, two flight engineers, one tactical co-ordinator, one navigator/communicator, three sensor operators, one in-flight technician and one in-flight ordnance crewman.

Sensors and Weapons

The US Navy has adopted an 'all DIFAR' policy in the use of passive sonobuoys, and the P3C carries mainly 'A'-sized DIFAR, the SSQ 53B. This buoy incorporates an autonomous function selection microprocessor, whereby the life and the depth may be selected, as may any one of the available 99 RF channels. For active acoustic operations, the Command Active Sonobuoy System (CASS) has been

PLATE 3.6. Lockheed P3C. (*Lockheed Company*)

replaced by the *D*irectional (DICASS) buoy, and the P3C carries the DICASS SSQ 62 buoy. This also has the ability to receive commands from the aircraft via UHF and to respond by sending target information to the aircraft via a VHF link. The command functions include deep-depth selection, scuttle, and selection of trans-ducer (sonic) transmission formats.

Naturally, the P3C also carries bathythermal buoys, the SSQ 36 and the omnidir-ectional active buoy, the *Ranger*, SSQ 47B. The P3A and the P3B versions of the *Orion* carry their sonobuoys internally in storage racks, but the P3Cs are fitted with a system of sonobuoy launch containers (SLC). These SLCs are external to the pressure hull of the aircraft and present a major disadvantage in that once the buoys are loaded, the channel, life or depth settings cannot be changed if the operational requirements change.

The P3C also has a MAD system and an air-to-surface radar (AN/APS-115) for locating submarines. Forward-looking infra-red (FLIR) systems complement the radar, but such systems are seriously degraded in conditions when there is a high moisture content in the air. However, once sure of the presence of an enemy submarine and given the right criteria for attack, the P3C can launch a selection of weapons from the internal bomb bay or from the 10 underwing pylons. The range of weapons includes the MK43, 44, 46 or 50 torpedo and depth charges.

P3C updates

The modernisation programmes to keep the performance of the aircraft as effective as possible while remaining with the basic airframe have been incorpor-

PLATE 3.7. Lockheed P3C. (*Lockheed Company*)

ated as several updates. From January 1975, Update I aircraft had new avionics and electronics software to improve performance. New equipment included a magnetic drum, increasing by seven times the computer-memory capacity; a versatile computer language; an *Omega* navigation system; improved acoustic processing sensitivity; a tactical display for two of the sensor stations; and an improved magnetic-tape transport.

In Update II, in 1976, the infra-red detection system was added, as was a sonobuoy reference system. From 1977, the *Harpoon* missile and control system were incorporated into production aircraft. Production deliveries of Update III models began in May 1984 and the improvements were mainly concerned with ASW avionics. New equipment included an IBM *Proteus* acoustic processor to analyse the signals from the sonobuoys and a new sonobuoy receiver to improve further the directional acoustic frequency analysis and recording system (DIFAR). Update IV is now (1991) being developed and will introduce yet further improvements in processing capabilities, a new Texas Instruments AN/APS-137(v) radar and a new family of acoustic sensors, designed to be effective against the improving quietness of Soviet submarines. A tactical ESM system AN/ALR-77 is also being considered for Update IV.

Many air forces are equipped with the *Orion*, albeit of various marks, but these include the anti-submarine aircraft of Australia, Canada, Japan, the Netherlands, New Zealand, Norway, Portugal and Spain. The Canadian version is the *Aurora*, externally identical to the P3C, with the same airframe and engines. However, the *Aurora* has the same telecommunications, radar, display and acoustic processing equipment as the US Navy carrier-based Lockheed S3A *Viking*. Of particular note, the radar is thought to be an improved model with better performance than that in the P3C.

THE BREGUET ATLANTIC

In 1959, the winning contender in a competition to find a NATO standard long-range MPA was the Breguet *Atlantic*. Although other national designs continued, an Atlantic programme was pursued by France and Germany, resulting in orders for a total of 87 airframes. France and Germany ordered 40 and 20, respectively, the Netherlands nine and Italy 18. All four countries participated in building the airframes, a European consortium produced the engines and Britain and the USA provided the avionics. Based on the efficient and reliable service from the *Atlantic*, the French decided in the late 1970s to re-open the Breguet production line and build an improved model. While this aircraft, now called the *Atlantic 2*, utilises the designs of airframe and engines of the original *Atlantic*, it has a completely new fit of weapons, sensors and displays.

PLATE 3.8. Avions Marcel Dassault *Atlantic*. (*Avions Marcel Dassault*)

The mission requirement for the *Atlantic 2* are basically similar to those of the *Atlantic 1*, including a high cruising speed to the operational area; a rapid descent from cruising altitude to patrol height; lengthy patrol endurance at low altitude; and an impressive manoeuvrability at low level. The aircraft can carry a comprehensive array of sensors and weapons for finding and attacking surface targets and submarines in any weather. The Thomson-CSF *Iguane* radar is quoted as being able to detect large ships at ranges of between 150 and 220 n miles and small targets, such as submarine masts, at over tens of nautical miles in rough seas.

PLATE 3.9. Avions Marcel Dassault *Atlantic*. (*Avions Marcel Dassault*)

The main weapons bay can accommodate all NATO standard bombs, depth charges and up to eight MK 46 torpedoes, seven of the advanced French torpedo *Murene*, or two air-to-surface missiles. A typical load comprises three torpedoes and one *Exocet* missile. The aircraft has four underwing points for the carriage of up to 7,716 lbs of stores. It can carry over 100 sonobuoys with a pneumatic launcher and 160 smoke markers and flares. The nose contains a SAT/TCT *Tango* FLIR sensor. The Thomson-CSF *Iguane* radar is retractable in its position immediately forward of the weapons bay. The MAD is a Crouzet version and is fitted in the lengthened tail boom. The ESM relies on a Thomson-CSF *Arar* 13A radar detector, and the processing of active and passive acoustic information is achieved by the Thomson-CSF *Sadang* system.

The profile of a typical anti-submarine warfare mission would be a take-off with four MK 46 torpedoes, 78 sonobuoys and a full load of marker buoys and flares; then a cruise at 25,000 feet and 290 knots to the patrol area; a descent to a low altitude patrol of eight hours at 600 n miles from base, or of five hours at 1,000 n miles from base; the subsequent return to base would be at 30,000 feet and the total mission time would be 12½ hours.

COMMAND STRUCTURE

There is no doubt that first-class equipment is essential for successful anti-submarine warfare. However, of equal importance is the command organisation and structure which directs and tasks these air assets as part of the co-ordinated anti-submarine effort. Again using the simple East–West divide as a background for an assumed scenario, it is most probable that Western maritime operations would be conducted within the NATO framework. That is, NATO as a coherent entity would respond to a perceived raising of the threat or heightening of tension.

Having therefore taken their place in NATO orders of battle, the MPA of the United Kingdom, the USA, the Netherlands, Norway and Germany would all work under the Commander in Chief Eastern Atlantic within the Atlantic Command. The capabilities and strengths of the aircraft would be combined in a cohesive force with a single chain of command. That command would also be unified in the sense that the Commander in Chief is a naval flag officer and the aircraft, whether they are in national navy or air force colours, work for that maritime commander, as do the surface forces and the submarines. The co-location of the surface, subsurface and maritime air staffs is a significant feature of a maritime headquarters. The senior air commander, the Commander Maritime Air Forces Eastern Atlantic, is a Royal Air Force air ranking officer, but he is subordinate to the Naval Commander in Chief. The staff of the maritime HQ which serves the command is made up of both naval and air force officers from all participating NATO nations.

A POSSIBLE SCENARIO

Intelligence and Tasking

The illustrative scenario must begin with intelligence and an accurate, piece-by-piece construction of the jigsaw which eventually grows into the picture of enemy dispositions above and below water. From as many sources as possible the intelligence officers gather their data and present their findings to the operations staff. In turn, the staff make recommendations to the commanders either for action based on certain intelligence or more reconnaissance to strengthen the validity of other pieces of information. One step is to decide whether to task an ASW aircraft to conduct missions independently or to send it to work in direct support of a surface group out in the ocean. Perhaps fleeting contact has been made on a possible enemy submarine during the night in an area where there are no surface forces. However, because the submarine might move to threaten such a force, an ASW aircraft would be tasked to locate, classify and destroy that submarine.

Planning

The task for the aircraft would be spelt out in a long, formatted message which would be sent to the maritime air base in good time for the base staff to use their mission support system to decipher it, consider it and order a specific crew to complete the task. The message would give the crew much information on their task, such as the likely position of the submarine, an area in which they could operate, positions of other forces, friendly or enemy, and the communications procedures to be followed. Having assessed the task, the weather in the area, the likely effectiveness of the several types of buoy in that particular part of the ocean on that day, the likely effective detection range on radar for the forecast sea state, the crew would discuss and decide upon a plan of action. After a last minute briefing on intelligence, the crew would go out to the aircraft, check that all systems were working and that all the required sonobuoys and weapons were aboard.

The Sortie

After take-off they would fly to the patrol area and set up their search for the submarine. The search would be conducted either by using radar, looking for the return from a set of masts above the water, or by using a pattern of sonobuoys and listening for the noise generated by the submerged submarine. It is most likely the crew would use a sensible combination of both systems, bearing in mind that blanket coverage of a large area with the radar is a very strong and clear signal to a listening submariner that an aircraft is in his area and may threaten him soon. The ASW crew may not wish their radar to transmit all the time. However, if it does and the submariner hears it and then departs or at least stays still, deep and silent, he may not be in a position himself to threaten any surface forces.

Tactics

Thus there is a cat-and-mouse element to this chase, as well as the factor that nothing is really clear-cut: there are usually shades of grey as well as advantages and disadvantages in adopting a particular search pattern. In this case, the opposite side of the argument may be that the aircrew will use their radar abundantly in an attempt to deter the submarine from snorting or surfacing. But a nuclear-powered submarine would not need to snort and may remain submerged for some considerable time. To him, a liberal use of airborne radar will be no deterrent and other tactics will have to be found. Thus the crew would have been keen to learn from their briefing whether their potential target was a conventional or a nuclear-powered submarine.

Patrolling their area, sweeping the surface intermittently with their radar and listening for underwater noise on their sonobuoy pattern, the crew will also have determined whether there are any radar contacts on the surface which may be enemy warships. If there are, a report would immediately be sent to the maritime HQ and the crew would attempt to clarify the type of ship. Not only would the information be of use to the HQ, but the crew would apply their knowledge about the type to decide by how much they should stay clear of the ship. For example, if the crew identified the ship as a *Krivak* frigate, they would know that the ships in that class carry the SA-N-4 surface-to-air missile with a range of eight nautical miles. They would therefore wish to stay out of, say, a ten-mile range of the ship's predicted position.

Detection

Suddenly, the acoustics team on the aircraft may announce that they have detected some noise on one or more sonobuoys. The crew would then turn towards that buoy in contact and assess the available information. At first there may not be much, but, as time goes by, the small snatches of noise, in terms of frequency and strength, can be pieced together to build a picture of the possible track of the submarine. Even no information on certain buoys may be positive information if the crew are satisfied that they have determined an accurate detection range. In other words, depending on the disposition of the buoys, no contact on a particular buoy could mean that the submarine was more than a certain range from it, a useful addition or supportive fragment of information.

Building the Picture

As the picture builds up, the crew will have some idea of the position of the submarine and will be able to decide where to place more buoys. These will gather extra information and either help to build the picture or even confirm what the crew already know. Soon the crew should have enough information to be sufficiently sure about the target's position, course and speed to be able to drop a homing torpedo. As always in these situations, there is plenty of scope for fine judgement: at which point should the crew employ active sonobuoys? As well as providing accurate range information, the active buoys alert a submarine that a hunt is in progress. The crew will have been careful up to this point not to have alerted the submarine. They will have avoided flying directly over his position, assuming that they make appropriate allowances for any inaccuracies in their estimate of such a position. Alerting a submariner unnecessarily could cost the ASW crew the chase.

More judgement is required in deciding when to drop weapons in the water: is there enough reliable information available as to where the target is and where he is going? Is there absolute assurance it is an enemy submarine? Whereas the crew will have to give due consideration to answering these and many other questions, they will nevertheless have to decide quickly what to do and get on and do it. Losing contact on a submarine while trying to decide what to do is very difficult to justify afterwards. But, assuming that the crew has progressed steadily if not rapidly through the distinct steps of detection, classification, localisation and tracking, the next phase is the kill and the crew select the required weapon and aim to drop it at the computer-predicted splash point.

Post-Attack Actions

The task is not over after the launch of the first torpedo: the crew will monitor its performance underwater to check that the motor is working. They will also want to know whether the torpedo has been successful, for if it has not, their job begins all over again as they attempt to relocate the submarine with sufficient accuracy to launch another attack, with, they hope, more success. Once satisfied that the target submarine had been destroyed, the crew would complete their patrol looking for others, and then return to base to report in detail all they have accomplished.

Another sortie may have been prepared to take over from them, either from the same base or, just as likely, from any of the other maritime air bases around the edge of the area.

TRAINING

In the earlier descriptions of the equipment fitted in the fixed-wing aircraft, it was too easy to give the impression that the equipment is good and that therefore the crew merely have to monitor the output and launch weapons on demand. While the equipment certainly *is* good, the difficulties of the environment and the assessment of all the information from a number of sources require that anti-submarine warfare crews be trained to a very high degree. They therefore practise continually, both in exercises large and small and in regular competitions among the ASW forces of the Commonwealth.

The peacetime role of maintaining a plot of movements and building a picture of the likely deployments of submarines and surface forces also helps greatly. While there are limits to what a crew might do in the event of finding a submarine in peacetime, the occasion would afford that crew some excellent tracking practice. Nevertheless, welding a group of 13 or so individual specialists together to produce a cohesive, effective team in a job as difficult as anti-submarine warfare is no mean feat. It needs constant attention and practice and crews need time to fly together and train in the simulator together before they can be considered an operational, efficient team.

The simulators available include faithful representations of the flight deck for the pilots and engineers and also of the rear crew compartment for the routine and tactical navigators, the air electronics officer and the sensor and communications operators. Crews are also required to study the recommended tactics for given scenarios and aims. Such tactics are generally the distillation of much experience, thought and discussion and are recorded so that the crews can turn to one source of wisdom on how best they might achieve the task set before them. A thorough working knowledge of these tactics is vital before any crew could contemplate the successful completion of their task.

SOVIET ANTI-SUBMARINE WARFARE

The Soviet policy on anti-submarine warfare is also one of co-ordination, involving aircraft, ships and other submarines. Again, the principal method of detection relies upon hearing sound waves underwater, and the ears of the Soviet aircraft are their sonobuoys. The Soviet Navy's ASW capability in the 1950s was restricted to a credible performance in controlling the waters close to its own shores: the capability was thus adequate but limited to short range. This limitation was thrown into sharp and dramatic focus in the 1960s when the first *Polaris*-armed submarines of the USA went on patrol. Having identified the problem, the Russians actively pursued a solution and their first step was to change their policy. They perceived a division of the task into two distinct areas: the near zone comprising a narrow strip of water close to their own shore; and a far zone reaching out from the near zone to the range of the missiles in the enemy submarines arrayed against them.

The vehicles for conducting ASW in the far zone were to be the hunter-killer submarine and the land-based, fixed-wing, long-range MPA. They had apparently thought that, for ASW tasks, aircraft were more effective than surface ships. Nevertheless, they did emphasise that ASW operations were joint affairs and that the best results could be achieved by combining the capabilities and qualities of each vehicle type. They also highlighted the advantages of the enemy SSBN as having a tremendous endurance underwater and a great capacity for remaining undetected. These advantages they saw as incentives for their ASW air forces to be kept at a state of high readiness and to be capable of matching the tactics of the submariners. It was not long before the Soviets concluded that great numbers of ASW aircraft would be needed in order to cover the vast areas of ocean and that the aircraft would have to work in combined operations with other forces.

Protection of the SSBNs

The 1970s saw the Soviets draw another sound conclusion: their own SSBNs, previously safe in their patrol areas and sanctuaries close to Soviet-controlled waters, would now need protection from NATO hunter-killers. To the fore of the minds of the Soviet planners must have been the *Delta* classes of SSBNs, with their SLBMs of more than 4,000 nautical mile range which permitted launch from the Barents Sea and the Sea of Okhotsk. The protection of these SSBNs was given to Soviet hunter-killer submarines, surface ships and ASW aircraft jointly. The Soviets were convinced that the potential of ASW aviation was increasing with this new role, despite the fact that their capability in open ocean still left much to be desired. They were convinced that aircraft would hold the key to these complex problems of detecting and destroying enemy submarines, even though they did admit that land-based aircraft suffered some limitations.

Soviet ASW Aircraft

Their primary concern was that the large and relatively slow ASW aircraft were vulnerable to land-based fighters and to shipborne surface-to-air missiles. However, in the early 1970s they introduced two long-range ASW aircraft and thus made great improvements to their open-ocean capability. The two aircraft were the TU-142 *Bear* F and the IL-38 *May*. The *Bear* F is a large, four turboprop-engined aircraft with the ability to carry sonobuoys, torpedoes and nuclear depth charges in its rear fuselage. The 'Mod 3' version, being the most common standard of the *Bear* F in service today, is fitted with a MAD boom at the tip of the fin. The aircraft has a maximum unrefuelled combat radius of 4,475 nautical miles.

The IL-38 *May* is also powered by four turboprop engines and carries a crew of nine. It has a search radar in an undernose radome and is fitted with a MAD tail boom. It accommodates a variety of sonobuoys and attack weapons and has a patrol endurance with maximum fuel of 12 hours. It has a maximum range of 3,887 nautical miles.

PLATE 3.10. TU-142 *Bear* F. (© *British Crown Copyright 1991/MOD*)

PLATE 3.11. IL-38 *May*. (© *British Crown Copyright 1991/MOD*)

Soviet ASW Sensors

Despite the steady increase in capability and size of the Soviet ASW air forces, their efforts were insufficient to counter the threat from the growing number of NATO SSBNs. The main reason was not only the growth in the number of these NATO boats but rather the poor performance of the Soviet ASW sensors. This trend has continued until recently, when it was held that, although the Soviet ASW aircraft are roughly equal to their NATO counterparts in terms of range, speed and endurance, their sensors and the processing capabilities were inferior. However, most recently there has been a growing suspicion that the Soviets have turned a corner in sonobuoy development and are beginning to make progress in improving their capability. Once again, the qualities of airborne forces are being enhanced by technological developments.

THE ANTI-SUBMARINE WARFARE AIRCRAFT: ADVANTAGES

Anti-submarine warfare is a complicated business. From an understanding of the environment, through an appreciation of the likely types of weapon systems to be encountered, to a working knowledge of the particular equipment and how well they might function, those who engage in this form of warfare need to have a wealth of material at their fingertips. They also need to understand how much the fixed-wing, land-based aircraft contributes to this discipline. Speed of reaction, flexibility in changing operating areas, and the ability to deploy sophisticated sonobuoys quickly are all tremendous advantages. Add to these the ability to interrogate the sonobuoys, process the information and then deliver an attack with smart weapons, and the aircraft is a formidable player in this complex game. However, the land-based ASW aircraft and crew, capable though they are, are only one group of players in a large ASW team.

Other members of the team include the intelligence staff, the allied hunter-killer submarines and the surface fleets. The surface fleets also include among their armoury ASW helicopters, with dunking sonar and the ability to drop and monitor buoys of the most common type. Anti-submarine operations from the decks of aircraft carriers are extremely effective and can sanitise large areas around the parent ships. Once again, teamwork is the key to success, but, to do it justice, the whole subject of carrier-borne operations is best left as a separate issue. Meanwhile, the land-based, fixed-wing aircraft employed in the anti-submarine role continue to give sterling service. Furthermore, their capability is continually being updated as technology allows more and more miniaturisation and greater airborne computing power. The size and complexity of the anti-submarine air forces around the world are a significant testimony to the importance of the role.

4

Anti-Surface Unit Warfare

DEFINITION

Anti-surface unit warfare (ASUW) is the sinking or disabling of enemy surface ships and is usually taken as action against warships rather than merchant vessels. Apart from the obvious basic attraction of afflicting attrition on the enemy and sustaining pressure on him in all areas, there are excellent reasons for conducting ASUW. Enemy surface ships may themselves constitute severe threats to friendly surface and submerged units, as well as being the means of delivering large and well-equipped amphibious forces in coastal assaults. Again, the interlacing features of maritime operations come into focus as an attack against a surface unit can form part of an integrated anti-submarine warfare campaign, if that particular surface unit is engaged in protecting its own submarines from marauding hunter-killer types.

FACTORS AFFECTING ANTI-SURFACE UNIT WARFARE

But the confusion created by the overlapping disciplines may be avoided by addressing several simple factors. These include the size of the target; the company of other ships around it; the self-defences of the ship itself and, naturally, of the group of ships; the position of the target; the required number of weapons to achieve the tasked level of damage; and, possibly, the role of the target.

If surface ships are tasked against opposing surface ships, one paramount consideration is the comparative range of the anti-ship missiles. Clearly the side which has the longer range surface-to-surface missiles can threaten the other, while remaining outside the reach of the enemy missiles. Furthermore, it may take the tasked ship some time to find its target and then manoeuvre into a safe position from which to fire its missiles. Finding the target, then keeping track of it long enough to mount an attack against it was certainly difficult in the Second World War. However, one advantage that aircraft enjoy over the surface ships is in the speed of reaction.

The Advantages of Aircraft

High-performance aircraft, whether they are launched from aircraft carriers or land bases, can cover the distance to the target in relatively quick time and deliver a swift punch. Land-based aircraft dedicated to maritime strike/attack are available at all times for their primary role, can carry heavier loads than their carrier-launched counterparts and can therefore carry more fuel to take their heavier load of weapons further. If the targets are initially assessed as being out of range of the land-based aircraft, then air-to-air refuelling provides the necessary support and increased range to allow the aircraft to reach the target and then return either to base or to a secondary refuelling base *en route* for home.

This speed of reaction and high weapon load give the aircraft distinct advantages even when it is flown from land bases. Not all the forces engaged in anti-ship attacks would support that statement: in particular, submariners claim that the sure way to sink a ship is to make big holes in the bottom of it and let in the water. However, these same submariners choose to ignore the slow speed of deployment of the submarine in moving into a target area, then manoeuvring into a firing position. They also tend to overlook the restrictions on communications with their shore headquarters or commanders at sea, imposed by their desire to remain submerged. They prefer to keep to themselves the way in which they resolve the fine balance between moving at speed to keep up with their target groups or remaining at a sedate pace to reduce as much as possible their tell-tale noise in the water.

Some Counter Developments

While land-based aircraft are better placed for communications and can cover long distances in relatively short periods, the balance of advantages over the enemy does not always swing their way. The potential effectiveness of an air attack has provided the incentive for navies to equip their surface units with a bristling array of anti-aircraft defences. Penetrating the extensive missile-engagement zones around well-equipped ships can be a dangerous excursion for an aircraft engaged in anti-ship attacks. The lessons of the Second World War all pointed to a long-range, stand-off weapon as the means to ensure a hit without exposing the delivery aircraft to the ship's defences. Fortunately for the aircrews, such a development has taken place: there are now several air-launched, anti-ship missiles which confer upon those crews the ability to fire their missiles in comparative safety from the ship-borne systems.

Naturally, ship defences have also progressed, whereby anti-missile systems are becoming commonplace. However, those defensive systems are not being fitted in isolation. Rather they form but one element of the armament of the sorts of ship which are most likely to be targeted by maritime strike/attack aircraft. Once more, study of the Soviet surface navy is profitable, as it yields examples of all the types of ship likely to be engaged by any ASUW force, should the occasion ever arise.

THE SOVIET SURFACE NAVY

The Soviet Navy made great advance under Admiral Gorshkov, and, while the submarine fleets have grown both in size and capability, the surface forces have also enjoyed expansion and improvement. Beginning with aircraft carriers, it was clear that the USSR perceived a need to equip itself with these major units for the projection of power if it was indeed to possess a worldwide ocean-going navy. More recently, it appeared that the Soviets believed in forward air defence provided by air-defence fighters operating from carriers. Early proof of the Soviet realisation that the Navy needed organic aircraft was the building and commissioning of the *Moskva* and the *Leningrad*, two helicopter carriers which were launched in 1965 and 1967, respectively. But the development did not stop there and the first of the *Kiev*-class aircraft carriers, *Kiev* herself, was commissioned in May 1975. The other three ships in the class are the *Minsk*, commissioned in 1978, the *Novorossiysk* in 1982, and the *Baku*, in June 1987.

The *Kiev* Class

Each one of the Kiev class is about 900 feet long, with a displacement fully loaded of 37,100 tons. It has an angled flight deck and is driven by four steam turbines. Capable of speeds up to 32 knots, it has a range of 13,500 miles at 18 knots and 4,000 miles at 31 knots. The complement is 1,200 ship's company plus however many aircrew are embarked. The surface-to-surface missiles are the SS-N-12, with a range of 300 n miles and with command guidance and radar homing. The warheads may be either nuclear (350 kiloton) or high explosive (1,000 kg). For air defence, the ships carry two SA-N-3 twin launchers for 72 missiles which have semi-active homing to ranges of 30 n miles at Mach 2.5 between altitudes of 300 and 75,000 feet. *Kiev* and *Minsk* have two SA-N-4 twin launchers for 40 missiles with semi-active radar homing to eight miles at Mach 2.5. The altitude range of the SA-N-4 is from 30 to 10,000 feet.

The *Novorossiysk*, and possibly the *Baku*, has sextuple vertical launchers for 96 SA-N-9 missiles. This missile is capable out to eight miles and up to 40,000 feet. As well as these formidable missile systems, the *Kiev* class carriers have four 3-inch guns each capable of firing 60 rounds per minute out to eight n miles. They also have eight 30-mm guns, which can fire 3,000 rounds per minute out to approximately one n mile. There are also the integral anti-submarine weapons, such as the RBU 6000 mortars, and the dual-purpose torpedoes, as though emphasising that these carriers are well-armed. Now add to this arsenal the aircraft themselves: the 12 Yak 38 *Forger* and the 21 *Hormone* A and B helicopters, and the *Kiev*-class carriers are well placed to act as the focus for carrier task-group operations. Their excellent command, control and communications facilities equip these ships for prime roles and, with the combination of all their weapon systems, they are the embodiment of the general-purpose ship.

However, the *Kiev* class does not pose an insurmountable threat as the *Forger* aircraft is limited in range and performance and it is not equipped with its own air-intercept radar. Thus all intercepts have to be controlled and managed from the ship. Furthermore, not all the airborne air-defence systems are capable against targets flying as low as 100 feet. Nevertheless, aircraft attacking such a target would undoubtedly fare much better if equipped with an effective stand-off missile.

The *Tbilisi*

A further step in the Soviet development of the aircraft carrier was the building and launching of the *Tbilisi*, a larger carrier than the *Kiev* and with a possible nuclear propulsion system. The ship will be renamed the *Admiral Kuznetsov* and there will be two other ships in this class, about 985 feet long and with an estimated top speed of 32 knots. They have a ski jump for the take-off of their organic aircraft, which will be variants of the MiG 29 and Su27. They will also carry the AEW, ASW and reconnaissance variants of the *Helix* helicopter. The role of the ship is likely to be very similar to that of the *Kiev*-class carriers but with clearly improved capabilities. For instance, there will undoubtedly be modern surface-to-surface and surface-to-air missiles on board, as well as short-range, anti-aircraft artillery systems. Furthermore, the ship will extend air-defence cover from the mainland and will complicate the ASW picture further away from Soviet territory.

The *Kirov* Class

Turning to battle cruisers, the Soviet Navy has three ships, and has launched a fourth, in the *Kirov* class. In Soviet terms, these ships are nuclear-powered missile cruisers and they constitute the first class of surface warships to be equipped with nuclear propulsion. They are the modern image in dimensions and speed of the old fashioned battle-cruisers and again assist in filling the Soviet need for self-contained, large, dual-purpose ships. They are 813 feet long, have a speed of 33 knots and can cruise at 33 knots for 14,000 miles. The second and subsequent ships of the class have a modified superstructure and armament but the basic weaponry of SS-N-19 and SA-N-6 missile systems remains the same. They carry 20 SS-N-19 missiles, which are capable of active radar homing at Mach 1.6 to targets at ranges up to 340 nautical miles. Their warheads are either nuclear or high explosive. The SA-N-6 is effective against aircraft out to ranges of 44 nautical miles and at altitudes up to 90,000 feet. The ships are also equipped with SA-N-4 missiles with an eight-nautical mile range against targets at between 30 and 10,000 feet. The last three ships in the class have SA-N-9 missiles, again with a range of eight nautical miles and maximum altitudes of 40,000 feet.

As for guns, *Kirov* herself has two 100-mm guns with a range out to 8.2 nautical miles; and the subsequent ships in the class have twin 130-mm guns with ranges out to 16 nautical miles. All ships in the class have eight 30-mm air defence guns firing out to a mile and a quarter. But the fit of the guns indicates that the operational intentions for the *Kirov* are far from clear: neither in calibre nor in number are they sufficient to provide gunfire support in scenarios such as amphibious landings. On the other hand, using the SS-N-19 surface-to-surface missiles would in those circumstances amount to overkill. When the SS-N-19 is used, its over-the-horizon targeting is provided by satellite communications or the *Hormone* B helicopter.

Kirov is herself in the Northern Fleet and, in support of a nuclear carrier, or as the hub of a task force comprising the *Kiev*, *Slava*, *Kara*, *Krivak* and *Ivan Rogov* classes, and being supported by the *Berezina* or the *Boris Chilikin* class, is a formidable, well-equipped ship, certainly able to defend herself against all but the most determined air attacks.

The *Moskva* Helicopter Cruisers

Now for more detail on the equipment and capabilities of the *Moskva* and the *Leningrad* helicopter cruisers. The two ships are 620 feet long and are powered by geared steam turbines. They can achieve speeds of 31 knots, and their typical ranges are 9,000 n miles at 18 knots, or 4,500 n miles at 29 knots. They are

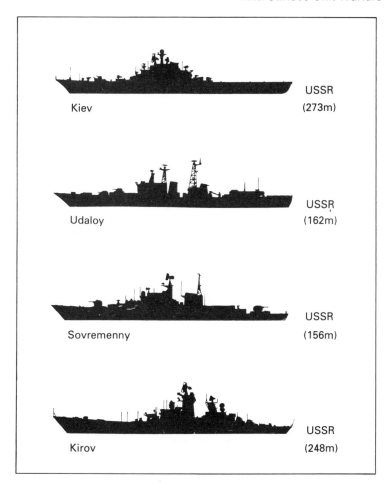

FIG. 4.1A. Silhouettes of Soviet surface warships.

equipped with SA-N-3 missile systems, with ranges out to 30 n miles at heights of between 300 and 75,000 feet. For guns, the *Moskva* class has two twin 57-mm mountings with ranges out to 3.3 n miles. The aircraft on board are 14 of the *Hormone* A, the ASW variant. The Soviets call these ships 'anti-submarine cruisers', and certainly the equipment is heavily biased for ASW work. However, with their communications and radar fit, the *Moskva* and the *Leningrad* have a useful, general-purpose capability, including command, air defence and ASW. One drawback is that both ships have poor sea-keeping qualities.

The *Slava* Cruisers

There are three ships in the next class, the cruisers of the *Slava* class, and there are reports of a fourth or even a successor having been laid down in 1986. The *Slava* class is 613 feet long and driven by four gas turbines, giving speeds of 34 knots and cruising ranges of 2,500 n miles at 30 knots, and 9,000 n miles at 15 knots. The main armament is the SS-N-12 missile, with active radar homing out to ranges of 300 n miles at Mach 1.7. The 16 missiles are carried in eight twin launchers. For air defence, the ships have eight vertical launchers for SA-N-6, the Mach 3, 44-n mile range missile capable of hitting targets up to 90,000 feet. They also have two SA-N-4 twin launchers for the semi-active radar homing missiles, of up to eight-n miles range at heights between 30 and 10,000 feet. The gun systems are the twin 130-mm mountings with ranges out to 16 miles and six 30-mm air defence guns. Operationally, the over-the-horizon targeting for the SS-N-12 is provided by satellite communications or the organic *Hormone* B helicopter. An observed drawback is that the capability of the SA-N-6 is reduced by the limitation of having only one radar director for the system at the rear of the ship. Nevertheless, the *Slava* is seen as a smaller, conventionally-powered version of the *Kirov* class and was designed as a back-up for them.

The *Kara* Class

Between 1971 and 1980 seven of the *Kara* class of cruisers were commissioned. These ships are each 568 feet long, powered by six gas turbines and can cruise at 34 knots, covering 9,000 miles at 15 knots, and 3,000 miles at 32 knots. The main weapon system is the SS-N-14 anti-submarine missile system, which has also been credited with a surface-to-surface capability. The missile deploys either a 450-mm torpedo or a nuclear depth bomb over a range of 30 n miles in the anti-submarine role or an high explosive warhead over 19 n miles in the anti-surface unit role.

For air defence, the *Kara* class has two SA-N-3 twin launchers for the semi-active radar homing missile, with a range of 30 n miles between 300 and 75,000 feet. As a variation on this theme, the *Azov*, fourth in the *Kara* class, has only one SA-N-3 launcher, the other having been removed to make room for the SA-N-6 missile with a range of over 40 n miles at altitudes up to 90,000 feet. All ships in the class have the SA-N-4 missile with a range of eight n miles between 30 and 10,000 feet, and the guns are the 76-mm version, with a range of eight n miles and the 30-mm air defence gun firing out to one and a quarter miles. With a *Hormone* A helicopter for the acquisition of submarine targets, these ships are classed by the Soviets as large anti-submarine ships. However, they do technically have a dual role with the surface-to-surface capability of the SS-N-14 missiles.

The *Kresta* II

Another class of large anti-submarine ship equipped with the SS-N-14 missile is the *Kresta* II class. There are 10 of these ships, which were commissioned between 1969 and 1977. Each is 520 feet long and powered by two steam turbines giving a speed of 35 knots with ranges of 10,500 miles at 14 knots, and 2,400 miles at 32 knots. The air-defence systems are the SA-N-3 semi-active radar homing missiles with a range of 30 n miles against targets at between 300 and 75,000 feet. For close-in defence, there are two twin 57-mm guns with a 3.3-n mile range and four 30-mm air defence guns. The *Kresta* II ships all have a *Hormone* A helicopter for anti-submarine targeting. Again, although *Kresta* II is primarily an anti-submarine cruiser, the SS-N-14 does also have an anti-surface unit capability.

The *Kresta* I

The predecessor of the *Kresta* II was the *Kresta* I which has now been designated as a missile cruiser. There are four ships in the class and all carry the SS-N-3B surface-to-surface missile, with a range of about 200 n miles and a choice of either a 350-kiloton nuclear warhead or one of 1,000 kilograms of high explosive. The ships were commissioned between 1967 and 1969 and are old enough to have the SA-N-1 air-defence missiles with a range of 17 n miles against targets at altitudes between 300 and 75,000 feet. They also carry two twin 57-mm guns, but only one of the class has the 30-mm air defence gun. This class was significant in that it comprised the first Soviet ships to be fitted with a helicopter hangar, thus providing it with a target-location facility which could be carried on board. It was therefore released from the need to rely on targeting information from shore-based aircraft and was able to use its own *Hormone* B helicopter.

The *Kynda*

A class of ship with no helicopter but with merely a landing platform for one to use is the *Kynda* missile cruiser. There are four ships in the class and they were the first to be designed as missile cruisers in the anti-surface unit role. Commissioned between 1962 and 1964, the ships were all modified in the early 1980s and are powered by two sets of geared steam turbines. Capable of achieving 34 knots, they can cruise for 6,000 miles at 14.5 knots, and for 1,500 miles at 34 knots. The main armament is the SS-N-3B surface-to-surface missile with a range of about 200 n miles. For air defence, the ships are fitted with twin SA-N-1 launchers and the 30-mm gun. They also have the 76-mm gun with a range of eight n miles. Targeting of the SS-N-3B missiles is a problem without a dedicated helicopter for over-the-horizon targeting, but the system relies in the main on the two *Scoop Pair* radars, one fitted on each mast.

To complete the catalogue of Soviet cruisers, the oldest class is the *Sverdlov*, with commissioning dates between 1950 and 1953. Mostly either in reserve or tied up alongside for long periods, there are nevertheless two ships of the class which act as command ships, having been modified with the addition of extra communications equipment. The main armament is the impressive looking array of triple 6-inch guns, of which there are three or four sets depending on the classification. Further variations among the class are found in the air-defence gun fits, and only two of the class have the SA-N-4 air-defence missile. Only one of the class has been modified with a hanger for a *Hormone* helicopter. Nevertheless, the class is worthy of mention because of the command function.

The *Udaloy*

The largest and most modern class of destroyer is the *Udaloy*, each ship being 531 feet long, with 12 hulls planned for commissioning between 1980 and 1991. The propulsion system comprises four gas turbines, giving a speed of 30 knots and ranges of 2,600 n miles at 30 knots, and 6,000 n miles at 20 knots. With a heavy emphasis on anti-submarine warfare, the *Udaloy*'s main armament is the SS-N-14 missile, with either a torpedo or nuclear depth bomb as the payload. The range of

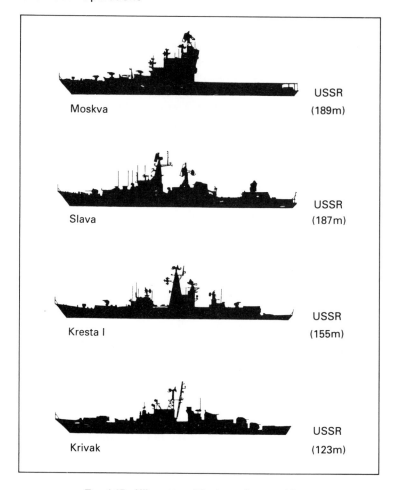

Fig. 4.1B. Silhouettes of Soviet surface warships.

the missile in this role is 30 n miles, it has a surface-to-surface capability when the range reduces to 19 n miles. The main air-defence system on board is the SA-N-9 missile, with a range of eight n miles against targets at altitudes up to 40,000 feet. For close-in defence, the ships are fitted with the 100-mm gun, with a range of more than eight n miles, and the 30-mm air defence gun. The ships carry two *Helix* A anti-submarine warfare helicopters. The *Udaloys* are assessed as being general-purpose ships, with the emphasis on anti-submarine warfare, and are seen as being complementary to the *Sovremenny* class of destroyer.

The *Sovremenny* Class

The *Sovremenny* class will eventually consist of 14 ships, the first having been commissioned in 1980 and the last one planned for commissioning in 1991. They are 512 feet long and are powered by two steam turbines, giving a 32 knot speed and ranges of 2,400 n miles at 32 knots, and 6,500 n miles at 20 knots. Being a specialist ship for anti-surface unit warfare, the main weapons are the SS-N-22 surface-to-surface missiles, with a range of 60 n miles and either a nuclear or a high explosive warhead. SA-N-7 missiles are the primary air-defence weapons and are effective against targets out to 15 n miles range at altitudes of between 100 and 46,000 feet. The guns are the 130-mm calibre type, with a range of 16 n miles and the 30-mm air defence version. The ships each carry one helicopter, either a *Hormone* B or a *Helix*. As a specialist anti-surface unit warfare ship, the *Sovremenny* class complement the ASW *Udaloy* class and the two types are often seen in company.

The Modified *Kashin*

The modified *Kashin* class consists of five ships of the old *Kashin* class modified to take the SS-N-2C surface-to-surface missile. Powered by four sets of gas turbines, the ships can achieve speeds of 37 knots and cover ranges of 1,500 n miles at 35 knots, and 4,000 n miles at 20 knots. The SS-N-2C has a range of 43 n miles and a high explosive warhead. For air defence, the modified *Kashin* has the SA-N-1 missile system, with a range of 17 n miles against targets at altitudes of between 300 and 75,000 feet. The complement of guns consists of the 76-mm version and the 30-mm air-defence version. These ships do not carry helicopters but are fitted with a platform at the rear. The main use of the ship has been in the 'tattle tail' role, trailing and marking prospective targets such as NATO battle groups in transition to war. The assumption is that should war break out, the modified *Kashins* would immediately sail away from their targets to the maximum range of their own SS-N-2C missiles, fire the missiles at the targets and keep sailing, hoping to escape retaliatory or even pre-emptive attack from those targets.

Other Destroyers

Other destroyers at the wrong end of the age and capability scales are classes such as the modified *Kildin* (three ships), the SAM *Kotlin* (eight ships), the *Kanin* (five ships), the modified *Kotlin* (five ships), and the *Kotlin*, (two ships). While these ships are very dated, and have limited capabilities, the Soviets have always believed that quantity has a value all of its own and they could bring them out in a major conflict.

The *Krivak* Class

The major class of frigate to mention is the *Krivak*, by now subdivided into the *Krivak* I, II and III types. This sleek-looking ship has gas turbine propulsion allowing a speed of 32 knots and ranges of 4,600 n miles at 20 knots, and 1,600 n miles at 30 knots. It was originally designed with anti-submarine and anti-air warfare in mind; thus both the *Krivak* I and II have the SS-N-14 anti-submarine missile system, with either a nuclear depth bomb or a torpedo as the payload. The missile also has a surface-to-surface capability. The air-defence armament is the SA-N-4 semi-active radar homing missile. There are a variety of guns depending on the mark of the *Krivak*, but essentially the *Krivak* I has the 76-mm type and the

Krivak II the 100-mm version. The *Krivak* III is different in major respects from the earlier versions in that it is designed for KGB use and does not have the SS-N-14 missiles, but has in their place forward a single 100-mm gun. The *Krivak* III also has a helicopter hanger at the stern and carries either a *Hormone* or a *Halifax* helicopter. There are 33 ships in the *Krivak* I and II classes.

The Soviet Navy operates many other ships in a variety of roles from fast patrol boats to small frigates, to missile corvettes and on to mine-warfare vessels and amphibious craft. But the major point here has been to show the range of types and the capabilities encompassed in the most important units of the Soviet Navy. It remains to add some words on their likely employment.

LIKELY EMPLOYMENT

In terms of appearance, the Soviet Navy is certainly menacing—the pure, almost artistic lines of the hulls, the arrays of capable weapons and the bristling outlines of the electronic aerials all combine to make the ships look businesslike and capable. Whether the ships are always fully manned with highly-trained and competent crews, whether they are all good weapon platforms in heavy seas, whether the systems themselves are reliable and whether the Soviet command and control system is adequate for the effective use of such resources are all questions which need to be addressed, but beyond the scope of this book. Nevertheless, it must be assumed that in war the Soviets would deploy their surface units to fulfil basic roles.

Two of the most obvious roles are, first, the protection of the waters in which the nuclear ballistic missile firing submarines would want to operate; and, secondly, the delivery and protection of a large amphibious force to capture and hold territory say, in the north of Norway or down the Baltic and on to the Jutland Peninsula. A third role might be anti-surface unit warfare in mounting a surface-to-surface campaign against an enemy in the Norwegian Sea and the north Atlantic. This role is seen as an extension of the defence of the homeland and protection for the nuclear ballistic missile firing submarines. In all of these roles the Soviet Navy is very likely to operate its ships in groups made up of specialist units, depending on the aims and the role of each group. One possible grouping is that combining the *Kirov*, the *Kiev*, the *Slava*, the *Kara*, the *Krivak* II and the *Ivan Rogov* class. A group like this would certainly pose a threat to an opposing carrier battle group were it allowed to get close enough. Groups with classes like the *Udaloy* and *Sovremenny* would threaten not only surface units but also their accompanying submarines.

The Response to a Threatening Surface Fleet

Faced with units, capabilities and possible intentions such as are exemplified in the Soviet surface fleet, anti-surface unit warfare must be undertaken by any nation or alliance contemplating general defence. And, for reasons touched upon earlier, the range of weapon systems available to engage in this form of warfare needs to encompass some element of airborne delivery of anti-ship weapons. The speed of reaction and the reach of land-based, fixed-wing aircraft, albeit relying on air-to-air refuelling, together with their extensive weapon loads make them formidable players in this part of the maritime scenario.

Vulnerability of Non-Combatant Shipping

Not only combatants but also non-combatant vessels are vulnerable to attacks from land-based, fixed-wing aircraft. Although the attacking of such targets may not appear as lucrative, the contribution to the war effort may be just as effective. In particular, long-range, land-based aircraft can threaten commercial shipping without the need for the extensive deployment of surface naval forces to enforce a blockade. Prior to hostilities in the Gulf in 1991, the United Nations forces conducted a successful blockade by combining air and naval surface assets. If the UN forces had been given access to more airfields, aircraft alone could have embodied the threat of offensive action and the naval force could have been reduced.

Combined Attacks

On the other hand, just because land-based, fixed-wing aircraft are effective in the anti-ship role, there is no reason to leave them to fight that particular battle single-handed if other assets are available for combined attacks. Such combined attacks could consist of weapons delivered by more than one aircraft type or nationality, by submarines and by surface warships. The advantages of these combined attacks accrue not only from the larger weight of weapons available for delivery, but also from the ability to launch simultaneous or near-simultaneous attacks from different directions, adding to the problem of the control of the targeted ship's defences. When the Gulf War of 1991 was at its height, Nimrod MPA were conducting surface surveillance for Coalition Naval Forces in the northern part of the Gulf. Part of their task (and achievement) was to provide targeting details for carrier-borne aircraft to attack and sink the Iraqi surface ships.

The Basic Responsibilities of a Maritime Headquarters

The co-ordination of these combined attacks or the straightforward tasking of an air unit for a single attack is the responsibility of a maritime headquarters, an organisation led by a senior naval officer but manned by naval and air staffs jointly. Whether the attack is to be a combined action or an operation for a single air unit, it would be the maritime HQ staff who would decide on the target and task the appropriate delivery systems or system. The staff would also organise tanker support for air-to-air refuelling if required, air-defence assets such as Airborne Warning and Control System (AWACS) aircraft and accompanying fighters and, most important of all, surface surveillance aircraft to provide last minute information on the position, course and speed of the target.

Location   Again, learning a lesson from the Second World War, the knowledge of an accurate and up-to-date position of the target is vital. Although anti-ship radars have made great advances over the past three decades, the open ocean is still a vast area, and effective surface surveillance remains a difficult and time-consuming task. One of the biggest factors militating against continuous radar surface surveillance is the certainty that there will hardly be enough maritime patrol aircraft available for anti-submarine warfare, let alone sufficient to spare for anti-surface unit search. The two roles are almost mutually incompatible. To conduct a thorough search of a large area for surface contacts, a maritime patrol aircraft has virtually to concentrate solely on that task and leave the anti-submarine role to come a poor second. The reverse is also true.

Co-ordination

Nevertheless, the maritime HQ staff have the authority to dictate priorities and, if an enemy surface unit is deemed worthy of the attention of an anti-ship attack squadron, then the priorities can be arranged to ensure that one or more MPA are available for surface search and direction. With the availability of modern command, control and communication systems, it is currently invariably the maritime HQ that will order attacks by specific units against particular targets.

Diversion of Effort   However, commanders of surface forces out on the ocean feel they need to retain the option of calling for immediate land-based air support should they require it to counter a threat undetected by the staff ashore. While the intentions behind such a provision may be laudable, the most likely outcome is a waste of valuable assets, with their sitting at readiness awaiting a call from a particular force when they could be more usefully employed attacking an enemy surface group, as directed by the maritime HQ.

5

Anti-Ship Aircraft

THE *BUCCANEER*

The types of land-based, fixed-wing aircraft available to commanders to carry out attacks against surface ships are many and varied. One of the most famous anti-ship attack aircraft is the formidable *Buccaneer*. This high-subsonic speed, twin-engined, low-level attack aircraft has been on the scene for many years. Crewed by a pilot and a navigator, the aircraft has long had a well-earned reputation for carrying a large weapon load many miles at high speed to a target. The aircraft was originally designed as a naval anti-ship aircraft, being equipped with the *Blue Parrot* anti-ship radar and a basic but effective bombsight for the long-range toss delivery of bombs. This delivery was supposed to keep the aircraft out of range of the defensive systems of the targets, but it takes no account of the subsequent vast improvement in ship defences.

The aircraft has been engaged in overland operations with the Royal Air Force as well as the original maritime tasks for the Royal Navy. Now the RAF operate the *Buccaneer* in the maritime role with two squadrons. Until recently, the squadrons had slightly differing weapons equipments, in that one was to carry TV and anti-radiation *Martel* missiles; and the other was to use laser-guided bombs and AR *Martel*. Both weapon fits reflect the need for as great a stand-off from the target as possible, while ensuring that a sufficient weight of weapons accurately hits the target to inflict maximum damage. The aircraft have been updated by fitting an inertial navigation platform and making some improvements in the radar and to the radar-warning receiver equipment. However, the most significant enhancement of the *Buccaneer*'s capability has been the equipping of the force with the *Sea Eagle* missile.

The *Sea Eagle* Missile

The BAe *Sea Eagle* is a subsonic, sea-skimming, launch-and-forget type of missile. Being approximately 13½ feet long and 15 inches in diameter, the missile is similar in shape and size to the *Martel*, which it was intended to replace. *Sea Eagle* is guided by its own inertial and radar systems and uses a turbofan engine for propulsion. With a range of about 55 nautical miles and a high explosive (HE) semi-armour-piercing warhead, the *Sea Eagle* combines all that is desirable for air attacks against ships: it has the guidance and capability to find its own way to the target once launched, it can deliver a damaging blow once it gets there, and, for the crews the most important of all, it can be released and sent on its way while the

PLATE 5.1. *Buccaneer* with *Sea Eagle* missile. (*British Aerospace*)

aircraft is still at low level well outside the range of the defences of surface ships.

The missile radar is a J-Band active-pulse terminal seeker and it can lock on to targets up to the radar horizon. The radar has a large acquisition area and there is thus no need for detailed aiming requirements before launch. The seeker searches simultaneously in range and azimuth, rapidly sweeping the designated area, and has a high probability of acquiring the target in a single sweep.

The reprogrammable computer controls pre-launch information, the transmit and receive functions, as well as the detection, acquisition and selection of the desired target, even if it is accompanied by other ships. The central processor, a Ferranti F-100L, also controls the flight trajectory in the modes of sea-skimming cruise, acquisition and terminal guidance. Another capability is that of identifying Electronic Counter Measures (ECM) activity and disregarding it. As the ship target moves in relation to the missile, the centroid return signal moves around the ship. However, this movement is represented as noise to the computer, which filters the information while continuing to focus on the centre of the target. For the sea-skimming part of the missile attack profile, a radar altimeter provides the height control.

Tactics *Buccaneers* appear to carry a standard load of four *Sea Eagle* externally mounted on wing stations. Thus a formation of four or six aircraft each armed with

PLATE 5.2. *Buccaneer* with *Sea Eagle* missile. (*British Aerospace*)

four missiles would constitute a severe threat to any surface group. Flying to an attack position as a cohesive unit or splitting into smaller elements and attacking the same target from different directions simultaneously would generate gross problems for the luckless target. Now that the *Buccaneer* is equipped with an inertial navigation system, such simultaneous attacks are within the realm of the possible.

Sortie Profile   A typical sortie profile might entail a task being generated by the maritime HQ staff for a *Buccaneer* squadron to attack a particular surface group in, say, the Norwegian Sea. The staff would first ensure that the precise position of the group could be obtained by ordering a series of maritime patrol aircraft to first locate and then shadow the group. Once knowledge of the groups' position had been confirmed, the *Buccaneers* would be launched with orders to make for a particular position prior to the target which was known by them and the patrol aircraft.

En route to that position, known as the 'gate', the *Buccaneers* might take on extra fuel from an airborne tanker and receive air information from an AWACS aircraft. They might just see some fighters tasked with providing air defence cover and they will certainly know the likely positions of any friendly forces in the area. However, they will not make any broadcasts on their radios, nor will they operate their radars, preferring to deny the enemy the ability to track them by electronic transmissions. As they approach the pre-briefed gate position, the *Buccaneer* crews will hear from the patrol aircraft explicit details of the target's position, together with any threats which may affect the attack. They would press on towards the target, release their *Sea Eagles* at some 50 nautical miles range then return home as quickly as possible to re-arm in readiness for another task (see Figure 5.1).

TV *Martel*

While the *Sea Eagle* was introduced as a *Martel* replacement missile, the RAF *Buccaneer* force can still carry both the TV and the anti-radiation *Martel*. These missiles were developed jointly by Britain and France, beginning in 1964. The TV version is nearly 13 feet long and is about 15 inches in diameter, having a small TV camera in the nose to relay a picture back to the launch aircraft via a radio link. The navigator in the launch *Buccaneer* has a small joystick with which he aligns cross-wires on his screen with the required impact point on the target. The missile flies a pre-programmed trajectory with a mid-course cruise height around 1,000 feet for a good TV field of view and to ensure that the launch *Buccaneer* maintains line-of-sight with the missile for the benefit of the data link. The *Buccaneer* carries a separate TV link pod on a weapon station which both transmits guidance commands to the missile and receives the TV pictures back from it. The missile has a high explosive semi-armour-piercing warhead.

Anti-Radiation *Martel*

The anti-radiation (AR) missile has the same structural components but is slightly longer, with a sharper nose than the glass-fronted TV version. The anti-radiation missile was designed against surveillance radars and has a blast fragmentation warhead. Three interchangeable homing heads were produced, depending on the transmission frequency of the target radar. The ranges are quoted as 10 miles for the TV version and 30 miles for the AR missile, but this latter range was calculated for the missile's having been launched from high level, about 40,000 feet. Currently the only operational delivery is one from low level, which would accordingly reduce the useful range.

Iron Bombs

The *Buccaneer* has in the past carried bombs for anti-ship attacks and these were at first the plain 1,000 lb high explosive 'dumb' bomb. Delivered in a toss attack, to avoid the necessity of overflying the targets, the bombs could inflict tremendous damage, provided one scored a direct hit. However, with the doubtful accuracy of a toss bomb, the probability of a direct hit, even from several *Buccaneers* tossing, say, four bombs each, was very low. Furthermore, the toss attack brought the

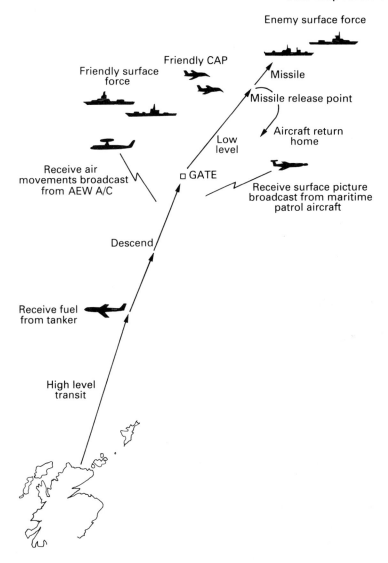

Enemy surface force

Friendly CAP

Friendly surface
force

Missile

Missile release point

Aircraft return
home

Low
level

Receive air
movements broadcast
from AEW A/C

□ GATE

Receive surface picture
broadcast from maritime
patrol aircraft

Descend

Receive fuel
from tanker

High level
transit

FIG. 5.1. Possible scenario for *Buccaneer* attack.

aircraft too close to the ship's defences, even if it did mean that the aircraft did not
actually overfly the target.

Precision Bombing

One solution to overcome the poor aiming accuracy was to introduce the laser-
guided bomb. With some form of designation of the target by a laser system, either
mounted in another aircraft or controlled by a third party, bombs fitted with laser
detectors and seekers would hit the source of the reflected laser energy. While this

method was a great improvement so far as accuracy was concerned, it did nothing to improve the chances of survival for the aircrew engaged in toss attacks against a well-defended target. However, one of the skills in anti-surface unit warfare is in the selection of a target in a surface group and the choice of weapons to use against such a target.

Specific Tasking

The likely targets are among those surface ships described earlier and probably to be found in groups. If that is so, and a *Buccaneer* formation is tasked against such a group, what should be the aim of the *Buccaneers*? The aim need not necessarily be to sink all units in the group. On the contrary, it may be sufficient for the particular scenario if a group were harassed and slowed down. Clearly, sinking a ship is the ultimate in harassment and delay, but achieving that sinking may be too costly an option for the maritime HQ. Harassment and delay could mean disabling the central capital ship; or removing all of the escorts; or identifying and then attacking a support ship with the oil and replenishment ammunition and stores.

A sustained attack against a group may even encompass all of these separate actions over many hours and several sorties by the aircraft. For instance, an air-defence ship placed up-threat between the capital ship and the likely approach of the attackers might be able to engage those attackers and even their missiles before they get close enough. The first aim may therefore be to negate the air-defence or sentinel ship.

In another scenario, the intelligence on a surface group may be so comprehensive that the attackers could plan to go around the air-defence ship and safely attack the central ship directly. Then the argument restarts as to whether the highest-value ship is the central ship, say *Kiev* or *Kirov*, or the oiler which is in support. With a variety of targets within one group it is worth pointing out that there may be a variety of ways of attacking it, depending on the target. Starting at the bottom of the scale, an intelligence-gathering tug, trawler or research vessel may be armed with nothing more threatening than a hand-held, heat-seeking missile. Hardly the target on which to use sophisticated stand-off *Sea Eagle* missiles in any number. It might be more profitable and a more effective exchange if a laser-guided bomb were to be used to sink an intelligence gatherer.

At the other end of the scale, a *Kirov* with a *Udaloy* and a *Sovremenny* for company would need a large number of stand-off missiles to be fired at them to reach any guarantee of success in inflicting damage without too great a loss of attacking aircraft. The principle involved here is weapon-to-target matching, and this art has assumed even more importance as assets become more expensive and therefore in great demand but short supply. Again, casting a thought back to the Second World War, this would be one of the advantages of maintaining sound and effective communications between air staff and the scientific research staff in order to ensure that estimates of likely weapon successes are based on reliable statistics rather than wild guesses. After examining likely target defences, the research staff could also advise on the probable effects of mounting the attacks as a mass raid on one axis or of splitting the force and engaging the enemy from two or more different directions simultaneously (see Figure 5.2).

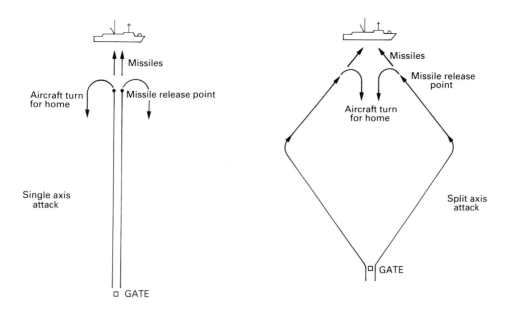

Fig. 5.2. Single and split axis attacks.

THE B52

Although the foregoing discussion has centred around the RAF *Buccaneer* and the weapons it can carry, the principles which emerge apply to all aircraft types and weapon systems involved in anti-surface unit warfare. For instance, another land-based, fixed-wing aircraft with a genuinely enormous range and load carrying capacity is the US Air Force's B52. Capable of carrying, then launching 12 *Harpoon* anti-ship missiles, the B52 has been involved in maritime operations since the early 1970s when there were several sorties flown per year on maritime surface surveillance tasks. However, in the 1980s this large, eight-engine, long-range and high-altitude bomber was given new teeth with the installation of equipment to carry and launch the *Harpoon* missile. Two squadrons of B52s are so modified.

The aircraft has a dual inertial navigation system linked with its digital search radar and weapons-delivery system. It also has an electro-optical viewing system, which consists of a low-light television camera and a FLIR sensor. For self-defence, the aircraft has four machine guns mounted in the tail and a comprehensive suite of electronic countermeasure equipment. It has, for instance, both receivers and jammers for land-based, shipborne and airborne early-warning, fire-control and intercept radars. The range of the B52G with the *Harpoon* is 6,500 miles.

The *Harpoon* Missile

The *Harpoon* missile, AGM-84A, is about 12½ feet long and about 13 inches in diameter. It weighs nearly 1,200 pounds and has a 480-lb high explosive blast penetration warhead. It uses impact fusing and inertial guidance and for terminal homing, employs an active phased-array radar. It is powered by a Teledyne XJ 402 turbofan engine with a flush air intake between the wing roots underneath the body. After launch, the missile flies a sea-skimming trajectory controlled by a radar altimeter. The range of the missile is about 65 nautical miles.

Third-Party Targeting   While the B52 armed with *Harpoon* might be a deadly weapon delivery system, capable of inflicting a serious blow at short notice and extreme range from a land base, the combination still suffers a crippling disadvantage. It lacks the means of finding and tracking the designated target with any degree of assurance. Thus, as with the *Buccaneer*/maritime patrol aircraft (*Nimrod*) combination, the B52 relies on targeting information from a P3C *Orion*. The surface picture intelligence gathered by the P3C is relayed to the B52, as well as the precise target information necessary for the attack. If a large group of surface ships were present, several successive P3C sorties might be required to guarantee the compilation of an accurate surface plot. Co-ordination of assets from two widely-separated air bases has long been a problem, but constant practice of well-thought out standard procedures should overcome such problems.

A Possible B52/P3C Tactic   One possible scenario using P3Cs and B52s with *Harpoon* involves the P3Cs' finding, then tracking the surface task force which is to be the target. At a pre-briefed time, the P3C drops two sonobuoys with an eight-hour life. The B52s, having departed from their base equipped with the knowledge of the likely area of the operation, arrive in that area and tune in their radio indicators to a pre-briefed frequency to receive a signal from the first buoy. They home to overhead the buoy and, as they do so, are observed on radar by the P3C. The P3C then broadcasts (in code) the range and bearing of the target from the second sonobuoy. The B52 flies to the second sonobuoy, again using radio homing equipment, and then follows the P3C's directions as to the range and the bearing of the target. At the release point, a designated distance from the target, the B52 releases the *Harpoons* and then turns for home. This scenario may be multiplied by the number of B52s tasked for the mission, say, three, and may be varied enormously in terms of where the sonobuoys are placed in relation to the target.

ARMING THE SHADOWER

Having discussed two systems for attacking ships with different aircraft and missile combinations, the common thread running through both is the fact that a separate, surface-search radar-equipped aircraft is required to provide the direction to the attack aircraft. This raises the questions, why should two aircraft types be required? Why should the attack aircraft not be capable of finding its own targets? If it were, it would require a radar system as large and as intricate as those fitted to the *Nimrod* and the *Orion* P3C. Furthermore, it would need an extensive range and endurance capability to guarantee its being able to stay in the search areas long enough to conduct a thorough search. These are not practicable nor cost-effective options for the sort of aircraft currently engaged in the attacking of ships.

But turn the question round and ask, in that case, why not arm the search aircraft? They have the radar for the search capability and they have the range and endurance necessary for searching the area. And the answer to this question is that both the *Nimrod* MR2 and the P3C *Orion* have been modified to carry the *Harpoon* anti-ship missile. The *Nimrod* can carry two of the missiles and P3Cs built to Update II standards and onwards have been fitted with the firing system for *Harpoon*. While the ability to carry and fire these missiles against a surface target is an undoubted advantage in terms of flexibility and multiplicity of roles, it does raise questions and generate its own problems. One rarely gets something for nothing in the world of aircraft and air-delivered weapons and the cost of loading *Harpoon* to either the *Nimrod* or the P3C affects the anti-submarine warfare weapons which have to be off loaded in order to accommodate these missiles.

The Balance of Effectiveness

This in itself could be justified if the scenario were such as to dictate maximum effort in the anti-surface role while ignoring, for the time being, the local anti-submarine task. But another factor comes into play and that is the number of weapons which the MPA can carry when compared with the number required to inflict satisfactory levels of damage on enemy surface units. Combining these two points, it may happen that, after all, the balance of effectiveness is gained by using the patrol aircraft as seekers of the target and directors of the attackers, leaving their own weapon fits totally dedicated to anti-submarine warfare, for the speediest transition back into that role once the attack aircraft have completed their mission.

Another approach is to estimate the minimum number of *Harpoon* missiles which might be needed to achieve success against a surface group. If the number is 20 missiles, four, five or six P3Cs would be needed to carry that number to a firing position. Taking that number of P3Cs simultaneously out of the pool of available aircraft for anti-submarine warfare would be a controversial step, depending on the priorities. The best way to look at MPA in the attack role is to consider that, using the great advantage of air power—flexibility—the option is available if required. If other factors combine to make the option viable or vitally necessary then it is worth pursuing. It may be a different matter in the future because of the advantages of designing, building and using a common, large airframe for a multiplicity of roles.

THE GERMAN NAVAL AIR ARM (GNAA) *TORNADO*

There are other examples of combinations of aircraft and missiles in use in the maritime air forces of today. The GNAA anti-ship combination is the Interdictor Strike version of the *Tornado* armed with the *Kormoran* air-to-surface missiles. The 90 *Tornadoes* form *Marinefliegergeschwader* (MFG) 1 at Jagel and MFG 2 at Eggebeck in Schleswig-Holstein on the neck of the Jutland Peninsula. With a maximum speed of about 600 knots and a radius of action of about 750 n miles the two MFGs are ideally situated for operations in the Baltic or in the North Sea. The self-contained nav/attack system combines a Texas Instruments multi-mode forward-looking radar with a Ferranti FIN 1010 three-axis digital inertial navigation system. It also has a Decca Type 72 Doppler radar system and a 128K central digital computer.

PLATE 5.3. GNAA *Tornado* with *Kormoran* missile. (*Panavia Gmbh*)

Tornado ASUW Weapons

The main weapon of the MFG *Tornado* is the *Kormoran* anti-ship missile, but the aircraft is also capable of carrying drag bombs, cluster bombs and *Sidewinder AIM9L*. *Kormoran* 1 entered service in 1977 and production continued until 1983. The missile has four clipped delta wings mid-body and four clipped delta control fins at the rear. The missile is nearly $14\frac{1}{2}$ feet long and about 13 inches in diameter. It weighs over 1,300 lbs, of which the semi-armour-piercing warhead accounts for about 360 lbs. In mid course, the guidance is inertial, then the terminal-phase guidance is provided by an active radar. Close to the target, the missile descends to just above sea level to hit the ship as close as possible to the waterline. Warhead initiation is delayed after impact to achieve maximum destruction inside the ship target.

Kormoran 2 For *Kormoran* 2, MBB have put more modern technological components into the *Kormoran* 1 case and have thus created a more effective weapon. The *Kormoran* 2 is also a fire-and-forget, sea-skimming missile with the same dimensions and shape as its Mk 1 predecessor. However, *Kormoran* 2 has a larger warhead, longer range, more launch modes and greater ECM resistance. It is due in service with the GNAA shortly. The size and the weight of the seeker, the processing electronics and the strap-down inertial navigation system have all been reduced by changing from analogue to digital systems. In particular, this has meant an increased warhead size, up to 485 lbs, with a new fuse and greater explosive power.

On leaving the aircraft, the missile is immediately powered by a booster motor. The higher power of this motor allows a significant cruise/glide portion of the flight profile until the speed falls to Mach 0.9, when a solid propellant sustainer-motor fires and propels the missile to the target. The extra power in the motors and the resulting longer glide mean that the range of the missile is over 18 miles when launched from an aircraft at 100 feet above the sea.

The active-radar seeker for *Kormoran* 2 will be a digitised, solid state, microprocessor-controlled system with a better performance than the *Kormoran* 1, an improved discrimination facility and better ECM resistance. The missile is, in effect, controlled by a 64K microprocessor and this programmable computer is fed with the aircraft's and the target's position before launch. During flight, it receives inputs from the inertial navigation system and the radar altimeter for control of the flight path at sea-skimming height, normally about 9 to 16 feet above the water. For the terminal phase, the microprocessor activates the radar-seeker for only the last two and a half to three and a half miles. Although this gives the radar only 15 to 20 seconds in which to find and acquire the target, it does reduce the risk of detection by staying passive until so late in the profile. Furthermore, a final change of trajectory ensures that the *Kormoran* 2 strikes the target just above the water line.

There are four firing modes planned for *Kormoran* 2: a radar-silent mode, where the target is acquired on radar outside of *Kormoran* range and the radar is then turned off and kept off while the aircraft closes to within *Kormoran* range and fires the missile; a radar firing, when the target information is fed to the missile by the aircraft radar's having illuminated the target at the launch point; a visual firing, where a target is acquired visually or very late because of an avionics failure; and an offset mode, where information on the target is acquired from another source, such as MPA and fed into the missile (see Figure 5.3).

THE F16 AND *PENGUIN*

The Norwegian anti-ship combination is the F16 *Fighting Falcon* armed with the *Penguin* Mk 3 missile. The F16 is a single-engine, single-seat, high-performance fighter equipped with a Westinghouse radar and an inertial navigation system. It can fly at speeds above Mach 2.0 and has a radius of action of more than 500 nautical miles. The *Penguin* missile was originally a ship-launched anti-ship missile and entered service in 1972. *Penguin* Mk 3 is the version which has been modified for use on the F16 and deliveries to the Norwegian Air Force started in 1987.

Penguin 3 has fixed, rounded leading-edge delta wings. It is 10½ feet long, has a diameter of 11 inches and the wing span is about 40 inches. It weighs 820 lbs of which 264 lbs are high explosive semi-armour-piercing warhead. Mid-course guidance is provided by the inertial system, and height keeping is controlled by the radio altimeter. There is provision for pre-programmed step changes in altitude and direction. The terminal phase is controlled by the passive infra-red seeker in the nose.

The F16/*Penguin* Mk3 combination would be used in the north Norwegian Sea

PLATE 5.4. GNAA *Tornado* with *Kormoran* missile. (*Panavia Gmbh*)

against surface targets detected and identified by, amongst other means, the Norwegian P3/MPA. The relatively short range of the F16 at low level would be no real problem in mounting attacks against amphibious groups aiming to land on Norwegian shores. Co-ordination would again be the key to the operation, with the F16s relying on information being collected by the P3s and then disseminated by the maritime HQ. The only extra complication with this particular weapon system is the choice of role for the F16: the aircraft may not be held in the maritime attack role. Thus a further step in the decision-making process would be required in deciding exactly when the system should be taken out of, say, the air-defence role and quickly loaded with the *Penguin* for ASUW operations. In effect, adding the *Penguin* missile does not take long and, once the decision was made, the aircraft and missiles would be ready in short order.

A more stringent complication is the limitation of the infra-red seeker. Such a seeker will not be able to detect a target through cloud or fog, and such poor weather conditions are common in the north Norwegian Sea. Thus there may be extensive periods when the *Penguin* would not be able to complete its final homing-in the most accurate manner.

SUPER ETENDARD AND *EXOCET*

Another anti-ship combination is the *Super Etendard* with the notorious *Exocet* missile. The *Super Etendard* was built by the French firm Dassault-Breguet, and

PLATE 5.5. GNAA *Tornado* with *Kormoran* missile. (*Panavia Gmbh*)

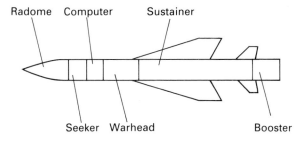

FIG. 5.3. *Kormoran* in detail.

PLATE 5.6. F16 with *Penguin* missile. (*Raytheon*)

this single-seat, transonic strike fighter was originally designed for carrier operations. The French Navy operate 71 aircraft and Argentina had 14. Although an update has been planned, the original aircraft had an *Agave* radar and a basic inertial platform and computer. The *Exocet* is but one of the weapons it can carry, others being the AN52 nuclear bomb, the BAP 100 concrete-piercing bomb and self-defence jamming pods, as well as a chaff and flare pod.

The AM39 *Exocet* is a medium-range, radar-guided, air-to-surface missile. The missile was first developed in 1967 as a ship-launched weapon, then the air-launched version followed in 1974, entering service in 1979. Designed as a weapon for attacking larger warships, the *Exocet* has been cleared for use by several aircraft and helicopters as well as by *Super Etendard*. It has four clipped delta wings at mid-body and four delta control fins at the rear. *Exocet* is 15½ feet long, about 13½ inches in diameter, and has a wingspan of three and a half feet. It weighs about 1,400 lbs, of which about 360 lbs is the high explosive shaped-charge fragmentation warhead.

The missile is guided by an inertial navigation system in the mid-course phase and a radar altimeter controls the sea-skimming trajectory at around 30 feet. In the terminal phase the missile can descend to about 10 feet above a calm sea and the guidance is then controlled by an active radar system. The propulsion system is a solid propellant motor and the range is reported to be 30 miles.

Exocet in the Falklands War

It was in the Falklands War of 1982 that the *Super Etendard* and *Exocet* combination gained such notoriety. This was the first time that air-launched, anti-ship missiles had been used in combat, and they achieved a devastating effect. Although the *Super Etendard* was designed and built as a carrier aircraft, the Argentinians used their *Etendards* throughout the war from land bases. This may have been because of their inability to protect an aircraft carrier from the British submarine threat, had the carrier ventured out towards the Falklands. Whatever the reason, the land-based *Etendards* flew many sorties, as did the *Skyhawks*.

Exocet v HMS *Sheffield* on 4 May 1982, two *Super Etendards*, each carrying one *Exocet* missile attacked HMS *Sheffield* off the Falklands. Flying at about 150 feet, they were directed to their target area by an Argentine P-2 *Neptune*. They approached from the south then climbed to 300 feet to acquire their specific target. At about 25 miles from the ships they detected two targets on their radar and fed the information on range and azimuth into the missiles. One missile was fired at each target but both missiles subsequently homed on to the *Sheffield*.

HMS *Sheffield* was acting as an air-defence picket ship, armed with medium range *Sea Dart* missiles. However, the *Exocet* missiles were able to complete their homing profile by turning on their radar for the final refinements of target position at six miles range. The captain and crew of the *Sheffield* saw the missiles during the final seconds of their flight, but by that time there was little to be done. Although one missile missed, the other hit the *Sheffield* amidships and drove its way into the operations room before the 350-lb warhead exploded. All main systems on the ship were damaged and the fire-fighting water supply was wrecked. Further damage was caused as the missile's solid propellant fuel burned, spreading dense smoke and heating the surrounding aluminium bulkhead until it was white hot. Four hours after the attack, HMS *Sheffield* was abandoned and she sank a week later.

After another three weeks, two more *Super Etendards* completed a similar attack against the *Atlantic Conveyor*, a British container ship. Having detected a large target, the aircraft released their missiles at the maximum range of 30 miles, thinking their target was a British carrier. Both missiles struck the ship and she caught fire and sank.

Management of Assets One significant feature among the many to arise out of these actions is that, at the outbreak of hostilities, the Argentine Navy had received only five of their hoped for 12 *Super Etendard* aircraft and only five of their *Exocet* missiles. Thus they were very careful in using these precious assets. First, there had to be guarantees that there was a target available worth attacking and, secondly, there had to be some assurance of a successful attack. These criteria led to their extensive use of the Boeing 707 transport and the P-2 *Neptune* MPA, both for reconnaissance and for command and control. The combinations worked well and ensured in particular that the *Etendards* did not have to expose themselves at 500 feet in searching for a contact. The initial search and detection had already been completed by the Boeing 707 or by the *Neptune*—the *Etendards* had to climb to 500 feet merely for target acquisition. As an aside, the ability for the

Argentinians to use the slower, larger targeting aircraft was a feature of the lack of clear air superiority by either side. It highlighted for the British the weakness in their not having a comprehensive airborne early warning system available.

Exocet v USS Stark

Although single incidents may be misleading, the Iraqi action against the USS *Stark* in the Gulf in May 1987 does at least demonstrate the lethality of air-launched missiles against surface ships. An Iraqi *Mirage* F1 fighter had taken off from its land base and was being tracked on radar by the USS *Stark* controllers for more than an hour. The *Stark* even detected the *Cyrano* IV radar when the fighter was about 27 miles away, but the chaff dispensers were not used, neither did the *Phalanx* anti-missile defence system operate. Two *Exocet* missiles struck the *Stark*, one fortunately passing through the ship without detonating. However, the second exploded almost immediately on impact and the resulting fire was so intense that parts of the aluminium superstructure melted. Again, smoke filled the ship and most of the communications were disrupted. The badly damaged ship eventually limped to Bahrain.

The principal lesson from the *Stark* incident was that the ship appeared to be unprepared to defend itself against what must have been predicted as a real and ever-present threat. The reported state of readiness of the ship and her company left a lot to be desired. However, the effectiveness of shore-based, fixed-wing aircraft carrying anti-ship missiles had been demonstrated very clearly.

SOVIET ASUW TECHNIQUE

The Soviet method of conducting anti-surface unit warfare is also founded on the principle of delivering stand-off weapons from ranges which guarantee safety from the defences of the target being attacked. The cold logic applied to the problem led to the design and construction of some early, quite long-range anti-ship missiles. The advent of these missiles also highlighted the problems of detection and of targeting of the ships. At the ranges envisaged, the targets were, in effect, over the horizon. Thus, over the horizon detection and targeting (OTHDT) became a challenge to be tackled through science, technology, organisation and tactics. The OTHDT system must be able to detect, identify and locate the target. However, it must also be capable of passing that information to the weapon system in time for an accurate fire-control solution to be utilised.

The range of systems which provide OTHDT include ocean-surveillance satellites, shipborne helicopters, surface warships, intelligence-collection ships, land-based radio direction finders, seabed sonar-surveillance systems and fixed-wing aircraft. Of all these systems the Soviets appear to prefer the fixed-wing aircraft and, specifically, the long-range maritime patrol and reconnaissance aircraft. The primary aircraft for the long-range wartime reconnaissance role is the *Bear* D, and one of its most important tasks is the pinpointing of surface targets for missile fire-control solutions on board ships or even in other aircraft. The *Bear* D is also able to supply targeting information for mid-course guidance of anti-ship missiles launched from surface ships and submarines.

PLATE 5.7. *Bear D.* (© *British Crown Copyright 1991/MOD*)

To detect these surface ships, the *Bear* D is fitted with the I Band *Big Bulge* A search radar, which has a capability against such targets out to a range of 85 nautical miles. Some reports suggest that the *Bear* D has a video data link with which to pass its radar pictures direct to the missile-carrying platforms.

But the *Bear* D is not alone in the detection and location role. The Soviet ASW aircraft such as the *Bear* F and the *May* may also be used as the eyes and ears for distant missile systems.

Soviet Missiles

The armoury of air-launched, anti-ship missiles carried by Soviet naval aviation aircraft is formidable and there are several fundamental differences between these missiles and their Western counterparts. The missiles are generally bigger, they are capable of flying out to much greater ranges, and their profile is not a sea-skimming pattern. Nevertheless, the missiles do pose a threat to surface shipping. The *Badger* C carries the *Kipper* with a range of 100 nautical miles and the modified *Badger* C carries the *Kingfish* with the greater range of 180 nautical miles. Modifications have made a difference to the range of the missiles carried by the *Badger* G: the unmodified *Badger* G carries the *Kelt* missile with a range of 85 nautical miles, but the modified version carries the *Kingfish*, with its longer range.

The *Bear* B and C carry the *Kangaroo* missile with a range against surface ships of 190 nautical miles. The *Bear* G, the *Blinder* B and the *Backfire* B all can carry two *Kitchen* missiles, with a range of 200 nautical miles in the anti-ship mode. The most recently acquired long-range offensive aircraft is the *Blackjack*, which carries the *Kent* missile with a reported anti-ship capability out to 1,600 nautical miles. The capabilities of the *Kingfish*, the *Kitchen* and the *Kelt* include their carrying a nuclear warhead.

WEAPON-TO-TARGET MATCHING

Finally, one of the common points in all maritime air operations applies critically to anti-surface unit warfare and is worth stressing again. With the high technological content of the weapons, the cost of using them could be astronomic. Thus accurate weapon-to-target matching is vital to ensure that only the right number of expensive weapons are employed. Such techniques require scientific research to be applied to the problem and the analysis will take several features into account, including the profile flown by the missile; the ability to counter any electronic jamming or deception from the target; and the lethality of the warhead. For the defences, the researchers will study the range of the shipborne anti-aircraft systems; the effectiveness of short-range anti-missile guns; the ability to deploy decoys; and the combined effort of several ships in a defensive screen around a high value unit. While the results of such studies may be initially hypothetical, they do provide a starting point from which operational commanders can begin the process of determining how many missiles should be targeted against a particular group.

ASUW PRINCIPLES

In anti-surface unit warfare, the principles of maritime air operations are clearly manifested: prior intelligence on likely targets is needed; accurate location information is required; precise weapon-to-target matching is recommended; and capable platforms and weapons are vital. Given these principles, land-based, fixed-wing aircraft are effective instruments in anti-surface unit warfare.

6

Maritime Air Defence

Having looked at the air threat to ships, it is appropriate for us now to ask how ships are to be defended against such air threats. Clearly the basic principles of air defence apply just as closely to the maritime situation as to any theatre on land. Leaving aside for a moment the vital question of available assets, the principles of air defence need to be explained in order to set the scene.

THE PRINCIPLES OF AIR DEFENCE

The Threat

In determining the principles of air defence,* the first step is to define the threat. Knowledge of the capabilities of the enemy, his weapon system, the training standards of his aircrews, the disposition of his forces and the capability of his command and control systems are among the factors which need to be assessed in order to determine his likely course of action. However, at this stage it may not be necessary to be too specific about the nature of the threat. It will probably suffice to assess that a threat exists and that therefore an air-defence system is required.

Concealment and Deception When it has been decided that a particular surface force is under threat of air attack, the next consideration is for that force to engage in concealment and deception. Concealment on the surface of the open ocean may at first hearing sound like a contradiction in terms. However, when linked with deception, concealment is a worthy cause in which to engage. Even if the general presence of the force may be difficult to conceal, knowledge of the precise disposition of units within the force may be denied to the enemy by constantly changing their relative positions. Some small groups may even be able to hide totally by sailing into bad weather, fog or low cloud. Others may be able to sprint to new positions during gaps in air-reconnaissance sorties mounted by the opposition. Any or all of these measures are of value.

Deception is the means whereby a ship or group of ships actively mislead an enemy sensor. The means are many and varied but may include radio transmissions giving false information. At the final stage of an attack, a ship may defend itself by deploying clouds of chaff. Chaff comprises strips of material designed to reflect radar pulses such that a false radar picture is generated by the attackers. If the

---

* A full detailed analysis of air defence may be found in Volume 7 of the Brassey's *Air Power* series, by Group Captain M.B. Elsam

picture can be sustained for long enough, the weapons may be seduced away from the real target on to the chaff cloud.

Emission Control   A more general approach to concealment is to confine radio and radar transmissions to the absolute minimum. This emission-control policy should mean that the enemy will not be able to rely on his receivers to detect the force. However, such a policy demands rigid adherence to standard operating practices. It also requires a promulgation of clear and unambiguous orders so that all elements of the air-defence system understand what they are to do, and when and where they are to do it. Thus a sophisticated form of secure communication is required or, if no transmissions at all are to be allowed, then a clear system of prebriefing signals needs to be known and practised by all parties. It will be no use having capable and expensive assets if they are not in the right place at the right time because of a failure of communications.

Detection of the Threat

Knowing when to order fighters to a particular intercept point is a function of threat assessment and early warning of that threat is vital. Detection systems to give as much warning as possible are normally placed as close to the source of the threat as can be justified. For a force at sea, this usually means an airborne early-warning platform for greater ranges of detection than ship- or land-based radars. This is particularly relevant to the detection of low-flying attack aircraft.

Offensive Defence   One sure way of removing a threat before that threat surprises a surface force is to attack the threat at source. The old adage about the best form of defence being attack rings true here. Rather than wait on board ship to control a defensive action for which fighters have been alerted by an early-warning detection of a stream of bombers, it would be preferable to attack the bombers at their base. Attacks against maritime bomber bases therefore make a significant contribution to the battle at sea, even though the attacks might be accomplished by overland squadrons.

Layered Air Defence   The principle of layering air defence systems is also vital. The probability that just one system would achieve one hundred per cent effectiveness against an incoming raid is remote in the extreme. Layers, on the other hand, are much more effective. Each layer may attempt to hit the raiders, and, crediting each system with some success, the final proportion of the raid getting through to the target will be considerably reduced (see Figure 6.1).

The Air Threat against Ships   The air threat against ships has been covered in the previous chapter, but to summarise: the major threat to surface shipping from land-based maritime attack aircraft comes from aircraft like the *Buccaneer*, the *Super Etendard*, the *Badger*, the *Bear* G, the *Blinder* B and the *Backfire* B. All of these aircraft carry air-to-surface missiles and thus the aircraft need to be destroyed before the missile release point or the defensive systems need to be effective against those missiles. On the other hand, the threat may also be

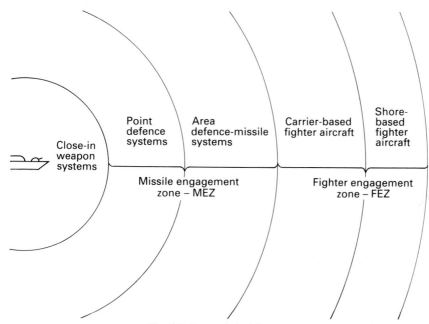

FIG. 6.1. Layered air defence.

embodied in the platform which provides the third-party or the over-the-horizon targeting for the attack aircraft. If the targeting platform can be brought down, if the surface fleet can somehow 'hack the shad' then targeting for the attackers is much more complicated.

Meeting the Threat

In meeting the threat from the air, naval surface forces will apply the principles of air defence. They will use a sophisticated command and control system to direct operations while as much as possible observing a strict emission control policy. The surface forces will deploy sensors well forward or 'up threat' to ensure that adequate and timely warning of any raid is acquired. They will then direct defensive weapons to intercept the raiders. A large, composite surface force will be able to provide most of the required assets from within its own resources. Carrier-based aircraft are available for airborne early warning and control, for strikes against land bases, and for intercepting and fighting incoming raiders, as well as the more sedate shadower.

The Advantages of Land-Based Aircraft However, land-based aircraft also offer significant features in their contribution to the defensive battle at sea. Land-based AEW aircraft are large, capable machines carrying large crews who man several control consoles. The aircraft can deploy rapidly to distant patrol areas and can loiter on patrol for several hours. The communication suites in the modern AEW aircraft are extremely effective both in clear and in secure transmissions.

As for fighters, the land-based interceptor can also transit rapidly to the combat air patrol (CAP) position and can remain on it for many hours, generally more heavily armed than his carrier-borne counterpart. The land-based fighter will generally need extra fuel from an air-to-air refuelling aircraft but, provided such support is made available, this need will not jeopardise the speedy performance of the air-defence mission. Clearly land-based fighters will always have to be airborne on a CAP position if the surface fleet is any distance from the fighter base. The need to rely on a land-based fighter held at ground alert to scramble in time to meet a rapidly closing threat is not an attractive proposition to any officer in tactical command at sea. He would rather use his indigenous assets or have the land-based fighters already airborne well up-threat.

The greatest contribution made by the land-based aircraft is in long-range, high-speed, long loiter time and high weapon-load capabilities, as exemplified in the AEW aircraft and in the fighters when supported by tanker aircraft. The fighters in particular make their contribution by forming the outer layer of a layered defence system around a surface force.

Overlapping Air Defence Responsibilities   As dictated by geography, one air-defence CAP ordered to protect one force may, at the same time, either purposefully or inadvertently, be also protecting another asset. A force of bombers when detected by an AEW aircraft may be heading in such a direction as to threaten a particular surface force. However, because of the geography and the tactical situation, the bombers may not be intending to attack that force at all. Their proximity to the force may be purely coincidental as they transit through the area to reach their assigned target beyond the surface force.

A strategically placed AEW aircraft, with its associated fighters on CAP and their tanker support, may effectively cover the approach routes to more than one target. The fighters may form the outer layer of more than one layered defensive system at a time. While this may appear cost effective, great care has to be exercised in stating priorities for the fighters and in organising contingency plans to ensure that one task is not pursued to the detriment of the other (see Figure 6.2).

LAND-BASED AIRBORNE EARLY WARNING AIRCRAFT

Boeing E3

The most well known airborne early warning aircraft is the Boeing E3A. This derivative of the 707 airframe with the rotating mushroom dome on top of the fuselage is now well established. Powered by four Pratt and Whitney turbofan engines slung in pods beneath the wings, the E3 carries a crew of 20, comprising a flight deck crew of four plus 16 command and control specialists. The fuselage contains communications, data processing and equipment bays as well as numerous multi-purpose control consoles and navigation and identification equipment together with a crew rest area and a galley.

The Radar   The elliptical cross-section 'rotodome' is 30 feet in diameter and six feet in depth, sitting some 11 feet above the fuselage. The radar is a Westinghouse

AN/APY-1 surveillance radar, which is housed in the rotodome together with the IFF antenna. During surveillance operations the rotodome rotates at 6 rpm but that speed is reduced to a ¼ rpm during non-operational flights to ensure adequate lubrication of the bearings.

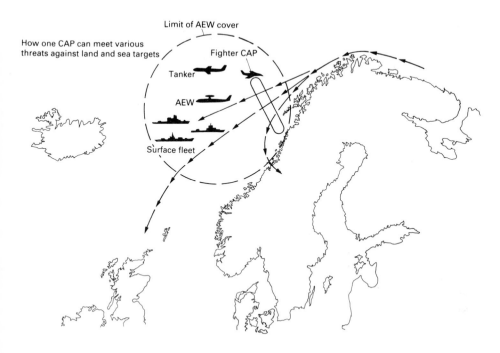

FIG. 6.2. Overlapping AD responsibilities.

The radar operates in the S Band and may be a pulse and/or a pulse Doppler radar to detect aircraft targets. The later models have had pulse compression and sea-clutter processing added to ensure success in detecting surface contacts on the sea. The heart of the aircraft is the IBM CC-2 computer and data display is provided by the *Hazeltine* high-resolution colour situation-display consoles. The main navigation system is built around two Delco AN/ASN-119 *Carousel* IV inertial navigation (IN) platforms, a Northrop AN/ARN-120 *Omega* set for continuous updating of the IN platforms, and a Teledyne *Ryan* AN/APN-213 Doppler velocity sensor to provide airspeed and drift information.

Communications The communications fit provides HF, VHF and UHF frequencies for transmission and reception in either clear or secure mode, whether in digital or voice formats. There is a weather radar in the nose and the IFF system is the Eaton (AIL) AN/APX-103 interrogator set. This set allows the operator to discern the range, azimuth and elevation, code identification and IFF status of all targets within radar range.

The aircraft is capable of speeds up to 530 mph and has a service ceiling of 29,000 feet. At a range from base of 1,000 miles it has an endurance on station of six hours. The maximum unrefuelled endurance is over 11 hours.

E3 Capability   This land-based, fixed-wing aircraft is an extremely valuable asset. From its position, say, out over the Norwegian Sea, it can compile an accurate and complete air picture covering many square miles, over both water and land. It can also discern surface contacts and shadow surface forces. The many control positions on board provide the ability to conduct several simultaneous tasks, such as providing early warning of attack to friendly surface forces or land units; controlling and directing friendly fighters to intercept such attackers; directing friendly attack aircraft on to their surface targets; and effecting rendezvous for fighters with their tanker aircraft.

E3 Vulnerability   Yet the positioning of this aircraft to accomplish these tasks entails its exposure to likely threats from opposing air forces. In detecting the approach of such an attack, the control aircraft is currently forced to turn and run to a safe area. Either that or at least run until the chasing fighters have broken off the attack through lack of fuel. Other possible solutions include arming the AWACS with self-defence missiles or providing it with a highly-capable escort of several fighters. But both solutions have disadvantages: no missiles can yet guarantee 100 per cent kill probability and thus many would be required to fend off a determined attack. Provision of a full-time fighter escort, particularly at a considerable range from base, would be extremely expensive in assets. The solution to the problem is being actively sought in several air forces.

The *Mainstay*

Another example of a land-based, fixed-wing airborne early warning and control system aircraft is the *Mainstay*, the Soviet IL-76 variant. Development of this aircraft was started in the early 1970s and more than 12 models are now operational. The four engines are Soloviev D-30 KP turbofans in underwing pods which can power the aircraft to a maximum level speed of 528 mph and a normal cruising height of between 30,000 and 40,000 feet.

The *Mainstay* has a rotating saucer radome mounted on top and towards the rear of the fuselage. It is fitted with an in-flight refuelling probe and carries a new IFF system and comprehensive ECM equipment. The aircraft was designed to provide the capability to detect and track aircraft and cruise missiles flying at low level over land and water. A combined force of *Mainstays* and Su-27 *Flankers*, the latest generation Soviet fighter, constitutes a formidable defence against aircraft threatening either the Soviet homeland or groups of Soviet ships out on the sea. Clearly, however, the problems which afflict the NATO AWACS aircraft also affect the *Mainstay*. Presumably Soviet defence planners are heavily engaged in devising methods of defending the *Mainstay* from the attentions of enemy fighters.

Another similarity exists between the NATO and the Soviet employment of these particular aircraft and that is in the consideration of their overlapping roles.

Just as land-based fighters from the United Kingdom on CAP over the Norwegian Sea could provide air defence for both a maritime surface force and the homeland, so a *Mainstay/Flanker* combination could provide defensive cover for a Soviet surface action group, as well as for the bases on the Kola Peninsula.

Tornado F3

Having detected the raid threatening the surface fleet, the AEW aircraft must now direct the fighters to provide the most effective air defence for that fleet. The fighters likely to be deployed forward from their land bases in Britain are *Tornado* F3s. This air-defence variant of the interdictor strike aircraft is basically similar to it but has a stretched nose to accommodate a larger radar, the GEC Avionics AI 24 *Foxhunter*. It also has a smaller stretch just behind the cockpit so that four *Sky Flash* missiles can be carried in two tandem pairs. It is powered by two RB199 MK 104 engines enabling an aircraft without externally-mounted stores to fly at maximum speeds of Mach 2.2 or 800 kts Indicated Air Speed (IAS). The operational ceiling is 70,000 feet and the unrefuelled endurance is two hours on CAP at 300 to 400 nautical miles from base. Clearly, with air-to-air refuelling the range from base to any CAP may be extended dramatically.

Foxhunter *Radar* The *Foxhunter* radar is a multi-mode, track-while-scan pulse-Doppler system using a frequency modulated interrupted continuous wave (FMICW). Integrated with the radar there is a new Cossor IFF-3500 interrogator and a radar-signal processor to suppress ground clutter. The system should be able to detect targets up to 100 nautical miles away and to track several targets simultaneously. Coming shortly, the Singer-Kearfott ECM-resistant data-link system, which is interoperable with other NATO systems, is under development for the *Tornado* F3. With its comprehensive avionics suite, the F3 can make a significant contribution to the dissemination of vital tactical information over a wide area.

F3 Armament The *Tornado* F3 is well armed, carrying four BAe *Sky Flash* semi-active, radar homing, medium-range, air-to-air missiles and two European built NWC AIM-9L *Sidewinder* infra-red homing short-range, air-to-air missiles. The aircraft also has a 27 mm IWKA Mauser cannon as a fixed installation in the starboard side of the lower forward fuselage. The four *Sky Flash* missiles can engage either high-altitude or low-level targets, down to 250 feet, in a heavy ECM environment and at stand-off ranges of over 25 nautical miles.

F3 Employment The all-weather interceptor can provide effective defence for a maritime surface force, whether or not an AEW aircraft has been tasked with maintaining a watch over the approaches to it. The numbers of aircraft readily available and the range from base of the desired CAP position will determine how easily a continuous CAP can be maintained to help protect the surface group. Clearly, with long ranges and therefore long transit times, a force of, say, 24 fighters would be hard pressed to maintain a CAP round the clock. Nevertheless, the commitment to defend both the United Kingdom and any surface forces in the

PLATE 6.1. *Tornado* F3. (*British Aerospace*)

Norwegian or the North Sea has been made. The commitment requires that the requisite number of tanker aircraft should be available to ensure that the operation is successfully sustained.

FORWARD BASING

One way to aid the provision of land-based fighters for distant CAPs is to use forward basing and deploy the fighters to allied airfields much nearer the likely action. While this move would greatly reduce the transit times to and from the CAP positions, it would commit the fighters to protecting only one axis of attack against the homeland. Thus a fine balance would need to be struck in deciding how many fighters to commit forwards; and the option is only available if the geography is conducive to such a move. For instance, if a NATO surface fleet was in the north

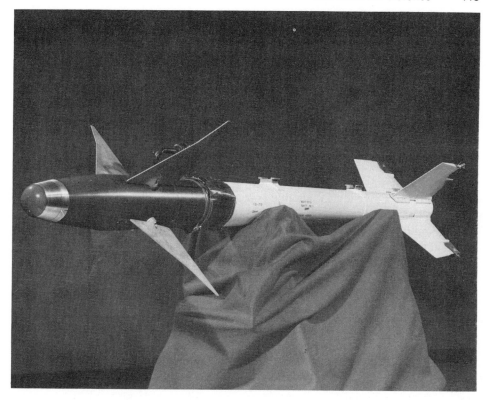

PLATE 6.2. *Sidewinder* AIM-9L missile. (*Raytheon*)

Norwegian Sea and required land-based fighters to fly CAP some distance to the north, some *Tornado* F3s might conceivably be deployed forward to bases in Norway. From there they could mount CAPs as required by the surface forces without long transit times in flying to and from their British bases.

Allocation of Priorities

However, fighters deployed to north Norway are no use in defending the British mainland from air attacks across the North Sea or from within central Europe. Furthermore, this book is too short for the sort of discussion required if one were seriously to consider, first, military deployments to Norway and, secondly, whether such deployments would affect the Nordic balance. The relevant, essential point raised by such matters is that of the command and control of fighters ostensibly attempting to meet two requirements. If the two requirements cease to overlap and actually conflict, then the command of the fighters must be clear and unambiguous to prevent contradictory orders from being given. In NATO terms, fighters assigned to one commander remain under his command until he is convinced of a more pressing need for them elsewhere and is prepared to release them for new orders. Nevertheless, the assignment and direction of shore-based fighters are subjects worthy of constant and close scrutiny to ensure that the maximum benefits are derived from aircraft.

SOVIET LAND-BASED FIGHTER SYSTEMS

Su27 *Flanker*

The latest Soviet fighter to feature in maritime operations is the Sukhoi 27, *Flanker*. *Flankers* are deployed to the Kola Peninsula in the northern Murmansk region of the Soviet Union. A supersonic, all-weather, counter-air fighter, the *Flanker* has a look-down/shoot-down, weapon-control system and beyond visual range air-to-air missiles. It is fitted with a large pulse Doppler radar and heavy armament which give it a formidable potential against low-flying aircraft and cruise missiles. The aircraft has two Tumansky R-32 turbofan engines, each with afterburner and rated at 29,995 lbs thrust. The performance figures include a maximum speed at height of Mach 2.0 and at sea level of Mach 1.1 or 725 knots and a combat radius of 810 nautical miles.

PLATE 6.3. SU-27 *Flanker*. (© *British Crown Copyright 1991/MOD*)

The nose radome houses a track-while-scan pulse Doppler radar which is reported as having a search range of 130 nautical miles and a tracking range of 100 nautical miles. Another sensor for locating and tracking aircraft is the infra-red system mounted in a transparent housing forward of the windscreen.

For armament, the *Flanker* is fitted with one 30-mm gun in the starboard-wing root extension. It can carry up to 10 air-to-air missiles, including the short-burn, semi-active radar homing AA-10A, the short-burn infra-red homing AA-10B, the long-burn, semi-active radar homing AA-10C, and the close-range infra-red AA8 or AA11.

Operating in conjunction with the IL76 *Mainstay*, *Flanker* is a potent example of a land-based fighter capable of playing a major role in the air defence of surface ships. Concern about overlapping roles may also worry Soviet defence planners, but their problems will be eased by two considerations. First, they may have larger numbers of fighters available, to allow dedication to one role or the other, i.e., ship defence or homeland defence. Secondly, the surface groups to be protected may not be so far away from the land bases. Another development worthy of mention is that a *Flanker* variant will be produced for the newest type of Soviet aircraft carrier, the *Tblisi*.

NATO LAND-BASED FIGHTERS

F16

One NATO fighter which can operate from its own land bases close to the surface groups in the north Norwegian Sea is, of course, the Norwegian F16. Already mentioned in the previous chapter, the F16 is a potent air-defence fighter, combining speed and agility with weapon-carrying capacity. The most common air-to-air missiles in use are the AIM-9 *Sidewinders*, and the aircraft also has a General Electric M61A1 20-mm multi-barrel cannon in the port side fairing between the wing and the body.

Employment of the Norwegian F16 in the maritime air-defence role is again a move which requires the most careful considerations and clear instruction. The aircraft may have several demands placed upon it, including ground attack, anti-ship attacks and air defence both of ship and of facilities on the mainland. Care in allocating assets and in defining the command and control responsibilities as between agencies ashore and afloat can overcome the problems. Nevertheless, as mentioned earlier, the arrangements need to be kept under constant review. On the tactical level, the integration of the land-based fighters into the maritime environment around a surface force with air support demands care and the meticulous observance of procedures.

AIR TO AIR MISSILES

Skyflash

Several of the missiles carried by air-defence fighters have been mentioned, and they share some potent capabilities. The *Sky Flash* on the *Tornado* F3 is a derivative of the AIM-7E-2 *Sparrow*, following the redesign of the semi-active radar seeker, the fuse, the autopilot and the power supply unit. The missile is 12 feet long with a body diameter of eight inches and a wingspan of three feet three inches. It carries a semi-active, J-Band inverse monopulse CW Doppler radar, which is credited with a good performance against fast, low-level targets in ground or sea clutter; the radar incorporates some electronic counter-counter-measure (ECCM) features. The missile receives signals from the parent aircraft radar via a reference receiver mounted in the rear. The warhead is a 66-lb HE continuous rod and the fusing is by active radar. The propulsion is generated by a solid propellant motor and the missile has a range of about 25 miles.

AIM-9 *Sidewinder*

The *Sidewinder* development programme began in the late 1940s and this very successful missile has undergone considerable enhancement since then. The AIM-9L *Sidewinder* marks the progression from the tail-aspect engagement only system to a capability to engage targets at any aspect. Furthermore, the AIM-9L embodies some stringent reliability features; thus it has a long storage life and can be carried on aircraft in flight for several hundred hours without defect. The missile has four swept-front control fins and four clipped delta wings at the tail. It is nearly nine and a half feet long, has a body diameter of five inches and a wingspan of just over two feet. It has an infra-red seeker with an all-aspect engagement capability and the 21 lbs blast fragmentation warhead is detonated by an active laser fuse. *Sidewinders* have been fired in conflict in the Middle East, Vietnam and the Falkland Islands.

AA10 *Alamo*

There are probably three versions of the AA10 *Alamo* which is a Soviet fourth generation missile. The variants of the missile employ either radar guidance or infra-red homing: *Alamo* A is thought to be a short-range, semi-active radar version; *Alamo* B is probably the infra-red guided version; and *Alamo* C is a longer-range, semi-active radar version. The *Alamo* has four fixed chamfered rectangular canards at the nose, four large trapezoidal moving control fins, and four fixed, clipped tip delta wings at the rear. The smallest of three variants is the *Alamo* B, the infra-red version, with a length of 11 feet 8 inches, a body diameter of seven and a quarter inches and a wingspan of about two feet three inches. It is believed that the infra-red version has mid-course inertial guidance and an infra-red homing terminal phase. The system probably has an all-aspect engagement capability as well as the ability to discriminate between decoy flares and the real target. The range is believed to be about 15 miles and the warhead is probably detonated by an active radar fuse. The *Alamo* A version, with the shorter range of the two radar variants of the missile, is similar in structure to the infra-red version, but the guidance section is longer with a missile length of 12 feet 11 inches. The *Alamo* C, the longer-range radar missile, has a larger motor section and thus the length of this version is just over 15 feet. Both versions of the radar missile have semi-active radar seekers operating in J-Band with Continuous Wave (CW) monopulse systems. The ranges achieved by these missiles are likely to be 15 miles head-on for *Alamo* A and 21 miles for *Alamo* C. The Su-27 Flanker can carry up to six AA-10 *Alamo* missiles as a mix of the three versions.

TANKER SUPPORT

The employment of land-based fighters in the maritime scenario is greatly enhanced and the length of time on CAP greatly extended by the use of tanker support and air-to-air refuelling. There are many options in such refuelling, but the most common approach appears to be fighters' taking on fuel *en route* to their CAP. Then they stay on CAP either until the next scheduled refuelling or until some event requires their attention. After such an event, the fighters take on more fuel and so the pattern continues until the off-task time. They then head for home and pick up more fuel to get them back to base.

These procedures make it possible to position the refuelling tankers well behind the fighters, where they may rely on the protection afforded by the fighters. Additionally, such positioning puts them in areas well covered by the AWACS aircraft and the radar of the surface forces. Complex tanker plans can be drawn up to ensure that there is always a tanker on station, well laden with fuel to give to the thirsty fighters. Transits to and from the tanker 'towline' may be flown in company with the fighters to ease the mechanics of refuelling the fighters *en route* to their CAPs.

The VC10 Mk 2 and Mk 3

The standard refuelling aircraft with the Royal Air Force is the VC10 K Mk2 and Mk3. This ex-passenger and freight aircraft, powered by four Rolls-Royce *Conway* turbofan engines has been converted into a tanker by adding remotely-controlled flight-refuelling units to both wings and in the rear centre fuselage. Extra fuel tanks have been inserted in the main cabin and the total fuel capacity if now 94,272 litres (20,737 gallons) in the K Mk 2 version and 102,782 litres (22,609 gallons) in the K Mk 3. All of the fuel except for that for the tanker's own mission requirements may be transferred. The aircraft can also take on extra fuel via the refuelling probe mounted in the nose.

Other Tankers

Other RAF tanker aircraft include the *Victor* and the *Tristar*. The *Victor* is much older and can give away less fuel than the VC 10K whereas the *Tristar* has enormous quantities to pass on to its customers. One concept envisages *Tristars'* refuelling VC10s and *Victors* and then those aircraft flying closer to the CAP positions to refuel the fighters. While the same amount of fuel may be available as from the original *Tristar*, the advantage of first transferring it to other tankers is that there are then more refuelling points available simultaneously for the fighters to use.

Soviet Tanker

The Soviet Tanker in most use is the IL 76 variant, *Midas*. This variant of the heavy transport aircraft is powered by four Soloviev turbofans and is fitted with a 'probe and drogue' flight-refuelling system. It is a three-point tanker with refuelling pods under both outer wings and a hose reel in the rear fuselage. The first operational *Midas* entered service in 1987 and the units fly in support of tactical and strategic combat aircraft. Whether the Su 27 *Flanker* is given an air-to-air refuelling capability and begins to operate with *Midas* tankers remains to be seen.

RECENT CONFLICTS

In the Falklands Campaign of 1982 the need for a complete and effective air-defence system was demonstrated most strikingly. Although the carrier-borne *Sea Harriers* and shipborne missiles were available and were used most effectively, the single component of the system which was lacking was an airborne early-warning capability. Quick to realise this, the Royal Navy pushed through very rapidly a modification to install a version of the *Searchwater* radar in several *Sea King* helicopters. Those *Sea Kings* then became the AEW facility for the fleet. However, the lack of comprehensive area coverage and the command and control capability of land-based AWACS, such as E3, remained a distinct disadvantage. There were no land bases within range to operate an E3, even if Britain had by then possessed such aircraft. However, it is worth noting that the E3D, the version of the Boeing AWACS ordered for the RAF, is to be fitted with an air-to-air refuelling capability. An E3D, refuelled in flight to and from the Falklands could have operated out of Ascension Island, albeit with extremely long sortie times.

As for the incident in the Persian Gulf when an Iraqi fighter fired missiles at the USS *Stark*, it has been reported that the AWACS aircraft on patrol at the time saw the fighter and warned the *Stark* of its approach. As was pointed out earlier, this incident serves to illustrate that all units should react quickly and comprehensively to approaching threats. It is not enough merely to have the assets available to provide the warning. Once given, the warning itself demands action. In the Gulf War of 1991, the Coalition Forces in the Gulf were constantly on alert against attacks by Iraqi aircraft. The defences included land-based and carrier-borne AEW aircraft and Air Defence fighters on CAP. There were no reports of Iraqi aircraft mounting any attacks which penetrated these defences.

COMMAND AND CONTROL

As already stated, it is vital to clarify the command of land-based fighters before they are committed to maritime air defence or kept chained to the basic defence of territory and land facilities. Having clarified who has command through the precise terms of assignment, the minute-by-minute control of the fighters is also important. Fighter crews need to know the current position of friendly surface forces in order to ensure that the former remain in their designated area relative to those positions.

A fighter will be allocated a zone in which he knows that if he detects anything unknown he is clear to engage and destroy it. Conversely, he should know the limits of the missile engagement zone: if he inadvertently strays into that zone, he himself may be attacked by shipborne missiles. He needs to know the frequencies on which to listen to and make contact reports. He needs to know the emission-control policy of the fleet he is supporting so that he can abide by it. Most importantly, he needs to know the threat sector he has been allocated to monitor so that he can fulfil his assigned task.

While all of this information is important when supporting one surface group, it is absolutely vital to have it before attempting to support a group which is close to or joining a second allied group, which might have slightly different orders and procedures. The risk of a self-damage encounter is extremely high and, once again, meticulous observance of the orders and procedures is vital.

TRAINING

Because the conduct of sorties from land bases but in direct support of surface forces at sea is so complicated, crews engaged in such sorties need to train regularly. The training needs to cover the precise actions demanded of the crews when transitting to and from a CAP and when on a CAP and a threat is detected. However, the crews must also acquaint themselves with and practise the procedures to be followed when co-operating with surface forces. While this training is possible in simulators and through the reading of manuals, there is no substitute for participation in large-scale, live maritime exercises. This is a truism for all types of land-based aircraft engaged in maritime air operations, but it is particularly relevant for the fighters since they invariably come so close to the position of their own forces.

SIGNIFICANT DEVELOPMENT

Thus in maritime air defence with land-based fighters, the biggest development since the Second World War has been the advent of the airborne early warning aircraft. Use of this all-seeing, fighter-control room in the sky has meant that fleets can react far more effectively against an air threat. The fighters themselves have developed enormously in terms of target-tracking ability, with radar and higher kill probabilities, not only from effective weapons but also from sophisticated on-board weapon control computers. The disadvantages of long transit times to CAP positions remain, but the ability of land-based fighters to provide the outer layer of air defence around a surface group is a bonus no surface commander should ignore.

7

Air-Sea Rescue

From the rescue operations mounted in the Second World War 13,629 lives were saved from the water around British shores and over 8,000 of these were aircrew. The Rescue Directorate had been set up in 1941, but it became clear soon after the war ended that the need for an efficient air–sea rescue service was going to continue. In 1947 the International Civil Aviation Organisation (ICAO)'s *Chicago Convention* laid down overall policies, procedures and minimum standard requirements for search and rescue (SAR). All NATO countries, as well as many others, are signatories to the agreement.

SEARCH AND RESCUE REGIONS (SRR)

The operational aspects of the requirements in the provision of a service are delegated to nations, with each nation taking on responsibility for SAR within a specific area or areas. These areas are *search and rescue regions* (SRR) and their boundaries generally coincide with the Flight Information Regions (FIR) (see Figure 7.1). Within each SRR, a Rescue Co-ordination Centre (RCC) is responsible for the efficient conduct of SAR operations, and, if necessary, it can co-operate readily with the RCC's in adjoining areas.

THE AIMS OF SEARCH AND RESCUE

The primary function of SAR is to save lives, and military SAR is aimed at saving military personnel. However, under the ICAO obligations, SAR is also provided for civil aviation. The secondary function of the SAR force is, subject to the availability of assets, to assist in the relief of maritime and general civil distress. In fact, the majority of SAR operations today serve this wider purpose.

Definition and Description

SAR is defined as a service provided by units to search for and rescue personnel in distress on land or at sea. The service or operation may involve aircraft, surface craft, submarines and special rescue teams and equipment. The service covers the whole sequence of measures co-ordinated and directed by a RCC to search for and

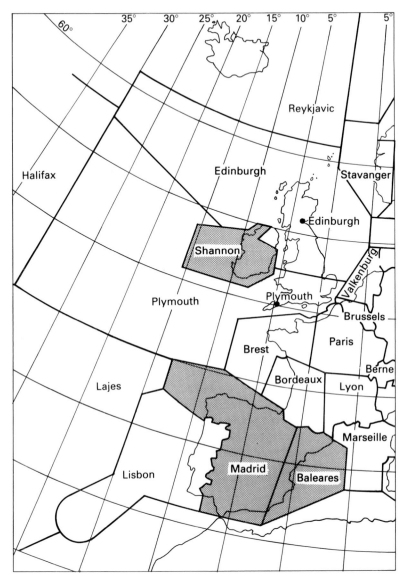

FIG. 7.1. Search and rescue regions.

rescue personnel in distress. On the other hand, a rescue operation conducted by local forces close to an airfield is not an SAR operation but is a 'local rescue.'

The Role of the United Kingdom

The United Kingdom is responsible for two SRRs covering the areas shown on the map at Figure 7.2. The RCCs responsible for the two SRRs are at Edinburgh and Plymouth. These two Centres will co-ordinate and control SAR operations in their own area either when an incident arises within it or when assistance is requested by an adjacent RCC.

RAF Facilities   The Royal Air Force supplies SAR cover for British and allied military aircraft and for civil aircraft. The areas involved are the two British SRRs and any other SRRs within which the RAF maintains units. RAF facilities may also be made available in any SRR by mutual agreement and arrangement with the national authority. Within the British SRRs, the RAF provides SAR cover, including: one *Nimrod* on one-hour standby, *Sea King* helicopters on 15-minutes standby, and mountain rescue teams.

Other Facilities   The Royal Navy also provides helicopters for SAR duties and there are marine craft available. These fast launches used to be under the direct control of the RAF, but they are now manned and operated by civilians who contract-out their services to the RAF.

Other facilities available to assist in search and rescue operations include RN fixed-wing aircraft, RN ships including an 'emergency ship' which is on approximately two hours-standby, and RN diving teams. The Army can provide fixed- and rotary-wing aircraft and people. There is the Royal National Lifeboat Institution (RNLI), HM Coastguard, the Police, the Fire Brigade and the Ambulance Services, coastal radio stations, as well as merchant shipping, civil aircraft and finally allied forces, such as the HH53C helicopters and C130 maritime search and reconnaissance aircraft of the United States Air Force.

Co-ordination   With all these facilities available, co-ordination is of prime importance to guarantee an effective and speedy rescue. The search will usually be controlled and co-ordinated by the RCC, but it may be that the number of participants and the scale of the rescue is such that the RCC cannot exercise control effectively. In this case, the RCC will nominate one of the search units to be the on-scene commander. He is then responsible to the RCC for the control of communications and the SAR operation at the scene of the action. The on-scene commander always remains subordinate to the RCC.

Search Factors   Once the RCC has been alerted that a genuine need exists and has decided to call upon the air assets available to conduct a search and rescue operation, the conduct of the search will depend upon several factors:

The accuracy of the datum, or how much faith can be placed on the first report. Was the report from a participant in the incident or a survivor and, if so, what navigational system did he use to calculate a position? If the initial report was from someone not directly involved but who was an observer, how did he assess the position of the incident? How long ago was the datum assessed?

Enhancement of the datum or the extent by which survivors could make the datum more obvious. The means of accomplishing this include visual aids, such as pyrotechnics and dye markers, and electronic or radio aids, such as radio-locator beacons.

The size of the target, for example, whether it is a crashed aircraft or a single person, and the environment or background. An orange, single-seat dinghy is quite

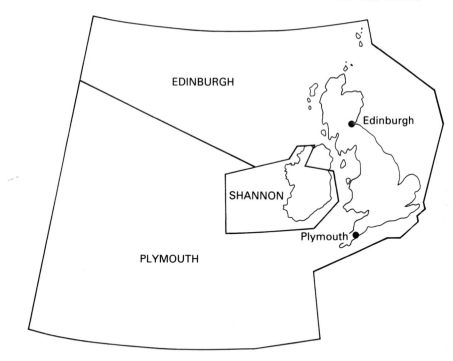

FIG. 7.2. UK SRRs.

difficult to see on the surface of a choppy sea, but it will stand out clearly on snow in bright sunlight.

The state of the weather will also play a part. Low cloud, mist or fog or even driving rain will restrict visibility and hamper a search. Similarly, a strong wind driving spray off wave tops will not help a search for a survivor in the sea.

The time of day will dictate whether the search is to be conducted in daylight or under cover of darkness. Night searches are not impossible provided non-visual aids are available such as radio beacons. However, searches in daylight will offer more opportunities to more pairs of eyes.

The number and types of search unit available will affect the conduct of the search, and, provided they are co-ordinated properly, the greater number of search elements available the quicker will an area be searched.

The time taken to search an area is a function of all these factors, which together determine the type of search and the size of the area to be covered.

TYPES OF SEARCH

Electronic Search

The easiest and generally the quickest search pattern an aircraft can employ is that used for an electronic or radio-locator beacon. If the aircraft is fitted with direction-finding (DF) equipment, the aircrew merely fly direct towards the beacon and keep refining the position as they pass overhead. As they descend, one of the

PLATE 7.1. *Nimrod*. (*British Aerospace*)

visual look-outs will eventually sight the survivor or the origin of the beacon signals. Even without DF equipment, an aircraft can home to a general 'on top' area by flying the procedure described in Figure 7.3.

Sector Search

When there is no locator beacon available but when there is deemed to be an accurate datum and the search aircraft can reach the datum in good time, the preferred search method is the sector search. Consideration of the factors previously discussed will guide the choice of leg spacing in terms of degrees apart around the circle. The factors will also dictate the radius of the circle to be covered. The advantage of this search is the abundance of coverage over the centre, the accurate datum reported to the RCC. See the diagram at Figure 7.4.

Expanding Square Search

If the area around a known datum is relatively small or if a sector search over a datum has been completed without success, the expanding square search is our next step. This is illustrated at Figure 7.5 and uses multiples of the track spacing to

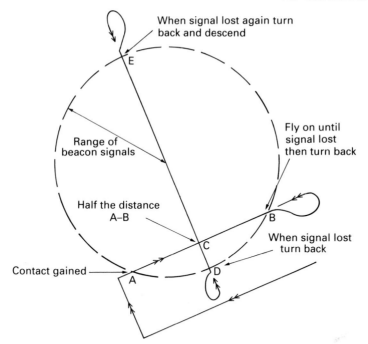

When signal lost again turn back and descend

When signal lost turn back

Fly on until signal lost then turn back

Range of beacon signals

Half the distance A–B

Contact gained

FIG. 7.3. Electronic search pattern.

determine the area searched. Track spacing is itself derived from the forecast and the calculated detection distance.

The Track Crawl

The track crawl may be flown when the intended track of the lost aircraft or vessel is known but the precise position of the incident along the track is not clear. The diagram at Figure 7.6 shows the plan of the search and, again, the spacing between the search tracks is a function of the calculated detection distance.

The Creeping Line Ahead

If the positional information for the search is poor, the area to be searched will expand dramatically. The creeping line ahead is illustrated at Figure 7.7. If the area is large but the detection distance and therefore the track spacing is very small, a variation of the creeping line ahead search can be flown, as is also shown in Figure 7.7.

The Nimrod *in the SAR Role*   The assets available for SAR in the United Kingdom were covered earlier but the specific attributes of the *Nimrod* MPA for SAR are extensive and worth listing.

The aircraft has an extensive communications fit, including HF, V/UHF, VHF(FM) and MF. It is equipped with a UHF D/F set and has a homer facility. It can carry the air-droppable survival equipment known as the *Lindholme* gear

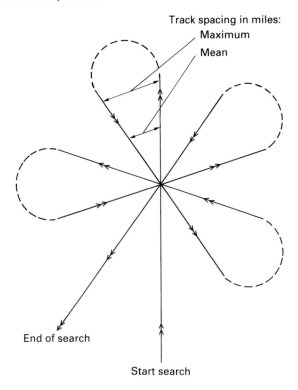

Track spacing in miles:
Maximum
Mean

End of search

Start search

FIG. 7.4. Sector search.

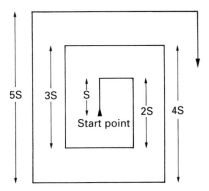

5S   3S   S

2S   4S

Start point

FIG. 7.5. Expanding square search.

comprising a large dinghy and many survival accessories. For an overland search, the *Nimrod* can carry container land equipment (CLE) in place of *Lindholme* gear. The crew may fire pyrotechnics and drop sonobuoys to aid homing to positions and the aircraft is also fitted with a powerful searchlight. The *Searchwater* radar,

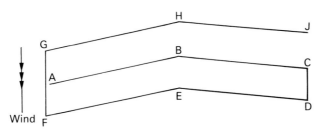

Fig. 7.6. Track crawl.

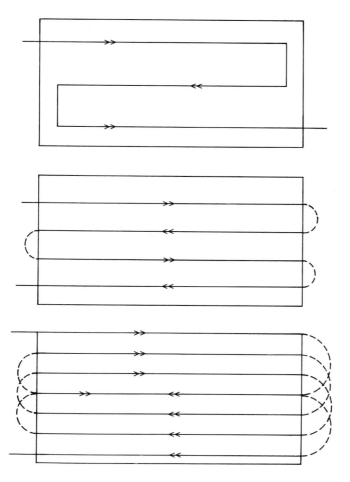

Fig. 7.7. Creeping line ahead.

described in Chapter 2, is ideal for detecting small contacts on the surface of the sea and has combined with it an IFF interrogator. Finally, but by no means of least importance, there are several visual look-out positions on the aircraft and usually a large crew to permit effective shifts of searchers to cover the designated area. The

Nimrod can rapidly fly a transit distance of, say, 1,000 nautical miles and then search a designated area for four hours before returning to base.

Sea King *Helicopter*   The *Sea King* helicopter is operated by both the Royal Air Force and the Royal Navy in the air–sea rescue role. The RAF uses the *Sea King* HAR Mk3 with a crew of four, comprising two pilots, an air electronics/winch operator and a loadmaster/winchman. The aircraft can accommodate up to six stretchers, or two stretchers and 11 seated survivors, or 19 people. The navigation equipment includes the Decca Tans F computer which receives information from the Mk19 Decca navigation receiver and a Type 71 Doppler. It also has a MEL radar.

The Royal Navy uses the *Sea King* HAS Mk5 in SAR and a further updated version, the HAS Mk6. The general performance descriptions of all the *Sea King* types are similar. The power is provided by two Rolls-Royce *Gnome* engines and the cruising speed at sea level is 132 knots. The ferry range with maximum standard and auxiliary fuel at 6,000 feet is 940 nautical miles. The all-important hoist facility is provided by the Breeze BL 10300 variable-speed hydraulic rescue hoist of 600 pounds capacity mounted above the starboard-side cargo door.

The significant advantages afforded by all marks of *Sea King* over their predecessors are, first, the night capability with the improved navigation and radar fit and, secondly, the automatic flight-control system with provides an auto-hover facility.

Likely *Operations*   In SAR it is often said that everything is different, no rescue is quite the same as any other. However, there are some common features among the statistics and a possible scenario entails the RCC's being alerted by HM Coastguard that a yacht is in difficulty. If the yacht is within range of a *Sea King* base and the RCC decides that urgent assistance is required, a *Sea King* will be despatched to assist and will, in the last resort, lift the survivors to safety.

If the yacht is too far away from a *Sea King* base then a *Nimrod* might be scrambled, first, to locate the yacht in distress, then to drop survival gear to those on board. The next task of the *Nimrod* will be to locate the nearest vessel afloat and attempt to communicate with it. The aim would be to let the vessel know somehow, by radio or visual signals, that a yacht was in distress and required assistance. The crew would fire and drop pyrotechnics to form a flare path towards the datum. As soon as the message was understood, the vessel should turn in the direction indicated by the *Nimrod* and sail to the stricken yacht with all haste.

Another scenario might involve a fishing boat in distress but at the extreme limit of the range of a *Sea King*. Then, once again, the duty SAR *Nimrod* might be scrambled to locate the boat and direct the *Sea King* to it eventually. The *Nimrod* would remain in the vicinity as an on-scene commander until the rescue had been completed.

A more pressing need for an on-scene commander would be evident in a major maritime disaster such as the *Piper Alpha* fire in 1988 or the capsizing of the *Alexander Kielland* rig in 1980. With many lives at stake, the weather bad and usually darkness prevailing, an on-scene commander in a position to talk to all agencies and to control the approach of helicopters is vitally necessary. The *Nimrod* with its long endurance and excellent communications is well able to fulfil this role. One of the most urgent requirements is in keeping all agencies informed as to what is actually happening on the scene. Based on these situation reports, the RCC can make well-informed decisions on what to do next or on what further services to call.

Whilst acting as the on-scene commander, the *Nimrod* crew can also allocate and control search areas for helicopters, fixed-wing aircraft and surface ships. Control of helicopters has even included the organisation and rotation of fuel uplifts from oil rigs in the vicinity of a rescue.

One fine decision to be made in such circumstances is on the use of the most valuable asset, the winch-fitted helicopter. In a major maritime disaster it is likely that several helicopters will be available but they will be a mix with some basic, utility helicopters and some winch-equipped types. While the rescue helicopters are the only ones able to pull people out of the water, they should be kept for that task only. Other helicopters or even surface craft may be used to ferry survivors to the shore or hospital. However, transferring survivors from one helicopter to another requires a landing platform close by and will invariably take more time. For some survivors, their condition may be so critical that their immediate removal to hospital is vital. Keeping them aboard the rescue helicopter and flying to hospital directly they have been pulled out of the water may save their lives but may also jeopardise the lives of those survivors still in the water. Each operation will have its own circumstances for the on-scene commander to handle.

US AIR FORCE HELICOPTER CAPABILITY IN THE UNITED KINGDOM

The US Air Force maintain a flight of Sikorsky HH53C *Super Jolly Green Giant* helicopters in the United Kingdom for SAR duties. These huge helicopters can lift 20 survivors at 600 nautical miles unrefuelled range from base. However, they are capable of refuelling in-flight from their associated C130 control aircraft, which obviously extends the range enormously. The crews include 'para rescue jumpers' who are trained parachutists, sub-aqua divers, first aid specialists, marksmen and survival experts. However, these helicopters take longer to get into the air than their RAF or RN counterparts who are on 15-minute standby.

SOVIET SEARCH AND RESCUE HELICOPTER

The Soviet shore-based amphibious helicopter employed on search and rescue duties is the MiL Mi 14, *Haze*. The helicopter has a boat hull planing bottom on the fuselage, a sponson on each side at the rear and a small float under the tailboom bestowing a degree of amphibious capability. It is the *Haze* C which is the SAR version, with a double-width sliding door at the front of the cabin on the port side with a retractable hoist. It has a searchlight on each side of the nose and is powered by two Isotov turboshafts. It can fly at speeds up to 124 knots and the range with maximum fuel is 500 nautical miles.

None of the Soviet maritime patrol and reconnaissance aircraft has been specifically credited with a SAR capability, but it is likely that aircraft such as the *Bear* F would fulfil a role similar to that of the *Nimrod*. The Soviet surface fleet is, as with the Western navies, well equipped with shipborne helicopters. Both the *Hormone* C and the *Helix* D are specific SAR helicopters.

CO-ORDINATION

Once again, the final point to emphasis in this area of maritime operations is co-ordination. No one element alone can provide all the necessary actions (alert, search, assist, communicate and rescue) required in an all-embracing, 24-hour, 365-days a year SAR organisation. Co-ordination between the alerting system and the rescuers and then between different rescuers is vital. With effective co-ordination, a speedy and efficient rescue may be organised, regardless of how many separate units are ultimately involved. The capabilities of the land-based aircraft and the commitment of their well-trained crews will once again have been put to good use.

8

Looking Ahead

INTERNATIONAL POLITICAL CHANGE

Any attempts to make predictions or even postulate likely developments for the future would be almost futile in the prevailing climate of dramatic change. While there are no signs that it is safe for all European countries to disarm, the changes in Europe, and especially the reunification of Germany, must lead to a general reappraisal of policies and strategy in international affairs.

But while the strength and capability of any military force maintained by a nation must reflect a perceived threat and therefore meet the specific need, the events in Europe will not necessarily mean a reduction in maritime operations. Maritime operations are conducted beyond Europe and, furthermore, there is no guarantee that freedom will replace tyranny everywhere in the world. The Gulf War of 1991 is a classic example of how oppressive and belligerent States can start a seemingly limited war which very quickly involves the major nations of the world. In that war, land-based maritime air operations were comprised mainly of surface surveillance then anti-surface unit warfare; but in future conflicts of a similar nature, the submarine threat may be strong and persistent.

Nations with global responsibilities or commitments may retain quick-reaction deployment groups ready to move rapidly to trouble spots when required. Furthermore, nations with large fleets of merchant shipping and heavily dependent on sea trade will want to retain the ability to defend such trade against marauders of whatever ilk.

Indeed, in May 1989, NATO leaders agreed and publicly stated their belief that the Atlantic Alliance contributes to Western freedom. They observed that the Soviet Union still has a remarkable military capability and confirmed NATO's policy of strength in defence. Arms control is seen in the West to have the principal objective of enhancing security and stability. However, there may be just a question mark over the true motives behind President Gorbachev's speech of October 1987 in Murmansk. The Soviet President then put forward a six-point plan for political progress in the North including a nuclear-free-zone in Northern Europe and restrictions on naval activity in northern waters.

The Murmansk speech may certainly be a gesture towards a reduction in arms and a manifestation of a genuine desire to reduce tension in accordance with the wishes of the Soviet, and for that matter, of all people. However, the USSR has become increasingly concerned with the adoption by the USA of a forward maritime strategy, which involves the pushing of large carrier battle groups into the north Norwegian Sea. The Soviet military built up in the Kola Peninsula is part of a chicken-and-egg escalation, but tension can run high in that area, and particularly when major exercises are conducted.

The proposals by Mr Gorbachev may be seen as a genuine desire to cut the size of the Soviet spending on defence, when pressures on the national budget are high. On the other hand, the size of the proposed cuts themselves did not appear large and could be accomplished by phasing-out older ships and submarines more quickly than originally planned. To achieve real cuts, the building of new ships and submarines should stop, but this has not yet happened.

Another of his aims may have been to portray the Soviet Union as the genuine peacemaker, both to gain credibility as a statesman and to wrest the initiative from the West in arms control talks. Despite scepticism about the speech, it has been observed that the Soviet Northern Fleet has spent less time at sea lately and any live exercises have been conducted much closer to home. Furthermore, the apparent disintegration of the Warsaw Pact as a cohesive, military organisation must encourage all those who wish to see stable peace in Europe without the presence of vast quantities of expensive armaments.

Whatever shape future developments take, the principles of maritime air operations will not change. Neither will the European and the American interest in the maritime environment change. With such a dependence on sea trade, such a perceived need for power projection across the globe, and such a firm belief in the capabilities of modern submarines as strategic weapon systems, maritime forces will be maintained for the foreseeable future. The specific exclusion of maritime forces from the Conventional Forces in Europe Agreements may be significant here. Maritime air operations will therefore continue as developments of their present day forms.

LIKELY RESIDUAL FUTURE REQUIREMENTS

Modernisation

When we consider the modernisation of any equipment in a specific role, it is too easy to fall into the trap of merely shopping for something similar which goes further, faster, for longer and carries bigger and more effective weapons. Because of the often crippling costs of new defence equipment, it should be part of a planner's discipline that, in forecasting when a particular equipment, be it aircraft, ship or submarine, is to be replaced, he should start a whole new thinking process. That process should begin with a clear definition of what the weapons platform is required to do in the most likely scenario. From that will come the guidelines on how it should do its task. Then, the all-important question may be asked: what is the best platform to fulfil this role?

This approach is the 'whole concept approach' rather than the mere 'replacement' approach, and cost effectiveness should play a large part in the essential decision making. Where the conceptual approach is most obvious in maritime air operations is in the consideration of the next generation of MPA. There may be scope, according to one school of thought, for combining all large aircraft requirements into one airframe. A nation might build one common aircraft type to cover such roles as maritime patrol, transport and airborne early warning. The increased number of the one type would bring the unit cost of the airframe down. Each airframe would then be fitted with equipment specific to its role.

The counter to that argument runs along the lines that role equipment is so complex that each role is likely to place significant demands on the basic airframe design. So much so, that the extent of the modifications to the airframe would cost more than the savings inherent in starting with only one airframe design in the first place. Added to that is the point that rarely do the needs of the various roles coincide to the extent that all necessitate new equipment at about the same time.

Another side to the argument on aircraft replacement is the question of whether a country should go it alone with its national design or whether it should buy off the shelf from the dwindling number of aircraft manufacturers in the international market. Although buying a guaranteed product from another nation may ensure delivery of a proven type, the offset arrangement for providing the buyer with work and profit-sharing are rarely satisfactory. Worse still, the indigenous industry may be deprived of sizeable orders and job losses could result, as may also loss of technology and expertise.

Yet further arguments are those for collaboration. In joining other nations, the advantages are again that the final order will be much larger than for an individual nation. The individual unit cost of each airframe is therefore much reduced. However, establishing the precise design to suit both or all nations involved is a time-consuming affair. The classic example of success in collaboration is the Panavia *Tornado* built by the United Kingdom, Germany and Italy. The European fighter aircraft to be built by the United Kingdom, Germany, Italy and Spain may be equally successful in terms of collaborative projects.

In the maritime role, there are few moves to initiate collaborative projects for patrol aircraft. The Americans were pursuing the P7 or the P3H, as updated versions of the highly successful P3C. The Germans have shown great interest in the P7, but the French have developed the *Atlantic* 2. The Dutch are considering their next move and the British are in a similar position, with options including purchase of whatever the USA choose, or the development of another British aircraft; or an American airframe with British equipment. Collaboration is not much in evidence.

Technological Innovation

Role Modernisation: Anti-Submarine Warfare Modernisation for anti-submarine warfare equipment is presently focusing on the qualities of the Lockheed P3H as the American replacement for the P3C *Orion*. However, airframe replacement is not the only development. With the advent of the quieter submarine and the subsequent dramatic fall in detection ranges with passive acoustic systems, exploration of other means of detection has been intense.

Techniques A laser-generated 'blue-green light' has been found to penetrate a considerable distance through sea water. Thus the way a submarine affects the pulse of blue-green light may be harnessed to provide a means of detection and location. For instance, once the generated pulse has struck a submarine, a sensor might then detect the reflection. Measuring the time between the transmission of the pulse and the reception of the reflected echo, and then after setting that time against the speed of the pulse through the water, the range of the submarine may be assessed.

Conversely, rather than reflect the pulse, it may be found that a submarine hull absorbs the pulse more readily than the surrounding environment. In this case, the submarine might be detected as a 'vacuum' among the more normal background clutter. The system suffers from the preponderance of false targets generated by optical systems, including marine animals. Nevertheless, it has been reported that Sweden is attempting to use a blue-green light system fitted to an aircraft overflying its national waters. No assessment of the effectiveness is yet available.

Perhaps of greater potential is the belief that a highly sensitive radar might detect the effect of a moving submarine on the pattern of the internal waves of the sea. The pattern of waves may be changed by the submarine disturbing the slow oscillation of water of different temperatures beneath the surface.

Patterns on the ocean's surface may be detected by some radar-surveillance systems, but to move on from that discovery to the point of using the information to locate submarines has so far proved difficult.

The US Navy has also closely examined the visible light given off by plankton and the pattern of light formed as an object like a submarine passes through the water and disturbs such lower forms of life. This effect is biological luminescence, and during the Second World War the effect was employed in that several surface vessels were detected because of luminous wakes.

Despite all these endeavours and the innovative thinking behind them, it is likely that for the foreseeable future, sound, or acoustics, will remain as the primary means of detecting and locating submarines in the sea. However, the story does not stop there, as the incentive generated by quieter submarines has placed the requirement for better noise-detection systems in the court of the anti-submarine warfare fraternity. One avenue for development is in the reduction of the effect of ambient or background noise. A major source of background noise is marine life. Marine mammals can produce low and very low frequency noises with enormous amounts of acoustic energy. An example is the blue whale, which is capable of generating 86 decibels, the equivalent of a large capital ship steaming at more than 20 knots. Identification and isolation of this background noise means that, in passive acoustic systems, such noise can be filtered out, leaving the submarine noise more readily detectable.

Seismic activity underneath the sea bed is yet another source of background noise which the US Office of Naval Research is studying. Again, identifying and precisely analysing this seismographic acoustic energy is only one step away from being able to filter it out from the noises detected by any passive acoustic system.

As well as attempting improvements in the means of acoustic detection, the areas where detection might be made are also potential sources of enhancement. Many modern submarines are designed to operate in northern waters beneath the ice cap. Indeed, their very reason for being there is so that they can loiter in their patrol areas and fire their missiles undetected, at least by aircraft or surface ships. But if some means could be found to penetrate the ice from the air for the deployment of acoustic sensors and weapons, the ice cap would no longer act as shield and protector.

Specifically for aerial use, a penetrator needs to be small enough to fit into current buoy housing, strong enough to withstand the considerable buffeting, capable of penetrating ice several feet thick, and docile enough to be handled safely on board an aircraft. Several ice-penetrating sonobuoy systems have been tried but only one appears to show features well suited for development. The technique is thermochemical ice drilling, in which a chemical medium exothermally reactive with water is put into contact with ice. The ice is destroyed by the direct chemical attack and the heat generated by the reaction. The drill itself would only be very simple with no moving parts and there are many chemicals which react exothermally with water. However, to be useful and effective an ice penetrator must use a thermochemical medium which reacts rapidly but not explosively with ice. It must also react rapidly but not explosively with water. Most important of all it must be reasonably safe to handle.

As for the sonobuoy part of an ice-penetrating system, it must be as close as possible in size, shape and configuration to existing sonobuoys to ensure compatibility and freedom of use without extensive modifications to current aircraft. Initial research has been into the means of dropping the sonobuoy housing and leaving it anchored in the ice while the hydrophones are deployed through the ice and into the water below. Eventually it should be feasible to make medium-sized holes in the ice to allow deployment of any of the equipment contained in a standard sonobuoy casing, and not just the hydrophones.

Aircraft   The replacement of any MPA is a complicated and costly undertaking. Not only has the airframe to be adequate, the equipment fitted to it has to be capable of meeting the stringent demands of the role today and in the future. The US Navy was considering the Lockheed P7A, an obvious derivation of the highly successful Lockheed P3C *Orion*. The P7 will have the basic P3 airframe design but will be fitted with new engines, avionics and flight-control system. The two most striking advantages over the P3C are the increases in payload and endurance. The P3, with two *Harpoon* missiles fitted externally, has a maximum payload of 22,200 lbs, while the P7A will be able to carry 38,400 lbs. In terms of sonobuoys, the P7A will carry 150 compared with the P3C which carries 84.

The P7A will be able to loiter for four hours at 1,900 nautical miles, or for nearly six hours at 1,600 nautical miles. The new engines will give better performance and will be much more fuel efficient. The aircraft will carry 120 pre-loaded sonobuoys in packs fore and aft of the wing and a further 38 internally. Control of the sonobuoys and, indeed, of the whole tactical system is being developed, but the new system is likely to be a step ahead of the P3C Update IV. Software in acoustic management and total system design is one area where improvements may be extremely effective without costing large sums for airframe modifications. However, the US Navy's interest in the P7 has ceased on cost grounds and speculation is rife that the next US Navy maritime patrol aircraft will be the P3H.

Another area of speculation concerns the choice of airframe and system to replace the *Nimrod* maritime patrol fleet. Should the United Kingdom build and equip its own aircraft or should it buy the Lockheed P7A or P3H off the shelf? If the United Kingdom bought a Lockheed airframe, would the government then insist on fitting it with British equipment? The answers to these questions may lead to another question, and that is whether there is any scope for a standing NATO MPA force.

Along the lines of the NATO AEW force, a NATO MPA force would certainly enjoy some advantages: the force would regularly operate under the same command and control structure whether in peace or war. NATO nations which could not afford their own independent MPA force could contribute to the NATO force and enjoy the benefits without meeting the whole cost. However, there would be difficulties, such as the lack of commonality if nations contributed one or two aircraft each, not necessarily of the same type. There is also doubt as to whether the facilities exist for NATO to purchase a squadron of aircraft with funds collected from members and then to man it with aircrew seconded from the nations. None of these problems is insurmountable.

ASW Weapons and Sensors   Developments in weapons, principally torpedoes, are likely to pursue the development of more intelligent and capable homing systems, as well as more effective warheads. With quieter submarines and larger and stronger hull casings, precise hits with penetrating warheads are necessary to inflict any sort of damage. As for sonobuoys, they too must continue to be as sensitive as possible and capable of detecting noise at specific frequencies at very low decibels. The quest for improvements in radar performance must focus on the detection of snorting submarines at greater ranges and easier highlighting systems for the presentation of the picture to the operator. Coloured screens for *Searchwater* on *Nimrod* are currently being introduced, for example.

Anti-Surface Unit Warfare   In ASUW, the question of aircraft replacement is again shrouded with many considerations. Maintaining a dedicated force of maritime strike/attack aircraft may not, in the year 2000, be cost effective. It may be that those aircraft, and their crews, would have to be capable of fulfilling two roles. For instance, a squadron of overland strike/attack aircraft may be given a secondary role in maritime strike/attack. However attractive this may be, the training of the crews will be vitally important and it will require tenacious dedication to ensure that the aircrew are as good as they need to be to fly the maritime task efficiently.

Another option might be to make a squadron into a maritime squadron, which flew air-defence missions as a primary role and missile-equipped strike/attack as a secondary role. The great advantage of such an allocation is that the squadron would always be training in the maritime environment, using maritime procedures and co-ordinating with other components of the maritime scene. The difference between the two roles is then essentially the crews getting to different missile-firing positions to release different missiles. The choice of a common airframe for the two roles may militate against this particular combination, but it is a point worth considering.

One suggestion for an aircraft to fulfil the ASUW role is the development of the large aircraft which can not only detect and shadow a surface force but can also carry and then fire several anti-ship missiles. This aircraft, by virtue of its size, might be too big and vulnerable to risk within range of the likely targets it might be required to attack. The vulnerability and lack of manoeuvrability of the large aircraft would be sharply relevant were the new breed of Soviet aircraft carrier to be given several Su-27 *Flankers* to carry and operate.

Yet another approach would be to rely on the constant availability of third-party targeting and intelligent missiles. These missiles could then be fitted to any aircraft which would successfully carry and fire them from a controlled missile-release position. It has been postulated that aircraft and crews from the more advanced training units might fill this role. It would be practicable provided that the aircraft had sufficient range or an air-to-air refuelling capability to reach the likely targets. Naturally, the crews would need to be sufficiently conversant with maritime operating procedures to be able to fit into the complicated scenario of co-ordination and support. Mistakes in that scenario may be costly in terms of self-damage between elements of forces ostensibly on the same side.

The best development for any nation seriously contemplating the anti-surface unit warfare role would be the acquisition of a dedicated, if small, force of high-performance aircraft capable of long range and carrying updated anti-ship missiles. Their capability would be evident and, possibly more importantly, their commitment to the role would be total, thus justifying their cost.

ASUW Weapons and Sensors   For the weapons used in ASUW, the developments required are, predictably, that the missiles should be capable of flying to a greater range and should have more effective warheads than at present. Furthermore, they should be capable of discriminating targets not only from within a group of ships but also from amongst the sophisticated deception and decoying devices likely to be deployed by future surface groups. Both the aircraft and the missiles should be capable of receiving data-link information direct from a third party designated as providing the targeting details.

Air Defence   The developments looked for in fixed-wing, land-based maritime air defence are to ensure that fighters are capable of long-range sorties. Additionally, their weapon-control systems need to be sophisticated yet user-friendly and able to operate in a hostile EW environment. Secure data link for rapid communications with all other agencies are essential and the systems must be compatible with the systems on other platforms. The radar should be continually developed both to extend the range of detection of the enemy and also to increase the number of targets able to be handled simultaneously.

Support Arms   In support of the Air Defence battle, the presence and capability of AEW aircraft are vital. More capability for the AEW in terms of detection, discrimination and control of friendly fighters is always the aim for the future. Protection for this valuable asset should also be on hand, whether by arming the aircraft with some smart advanced missiles or by providing a fighter escort.

The tanker support is equally vital if the CAP positions are at long ranges from the shore base. This support can be developed by extending not only the amount of fuel available for giving away, but also the number of refuelling points per tanker. This ensures that simultaneous off-loading for several fighters is feasible.

Air–Sea Rescue   For air–sea rescue, there are already some capable helicopters and fixed-wing aircraft available. However, improvements in this area might include yet longer ranges for the helicopters and provision of the most advanced night-illumination devices to aid rescues in the dark. Furthermore, navigational accuracy could be greatly enhanced by fitting the aircraft with satellite-based navigation aids.

Communications are important in any rescue but in a large-scale rescue involving many units they are absolutely vital. Communications equipment in the air–sea rescue aircraft must keep pace with the developments in offshore industries as well as in shipping organisations.

The development of techniques is also important, particularly in the realm of combat search and rescue.

CONCLUSIONS

The scope of land-based, fixed-wing and helicopter maritime air operations is enormous. Regardless of any drastic changes to the political and military structures in Europe, maritime air operations from land bases will still be required. The range, information-processing and weapon-carrying capabilities, and flexibility of land-based aircraft ensures them a secure place in maritime operations for some considerable time to come.

Self-Test Questions

Chapter 1 The Nature of Maritime Air Operations
1. Define maritime air operations.
2. Describe the roles of the submarine today and compare them with the role of the U-boats in World War Two.
3. Which single weapon system makes anti-ship attacks by aircraft realistic?
4. What are the advantages of land-based, fixed-wing aircraft employed on maritime surveillance?
5. Which feature of maritime air-defence systems is considered the most important and why?
6. List some of the limitations of anti-submarine aircraft and weapon systems in use in the early days of World War Two.
7. Describe the circumstances in anti-submarine warfare leading to the development of the searchlight fitted to aircraft.
8. List the improvements to the Allied anti-submarine warfare capabilities which turned the tide against the U-boat packs.
9. Describe the World War Two methods for detecting and attacking submarines from aircraft.
10. Why were casualty rates so high among aircraft and crews attacking surface ships in World War Two?
11. What were the principles governing maritime air defence in World War Two?
12. What were the features of an effective air–sea rescue service in World War Two?

Chapter 2 Anti-Submarine Warfare
1. What is the aim of modern anti-submarine warfare forces?
2. Describe the Soviet *Typhoon*-class submarine.
3. List the advantages and disadvantages of nuclear-powered submarines compared with their conventional counterparts.
4. Describe the three main factors which affect the velocity of sound waves in water.
5. Describe passive and active acoustic detection.
6. Which system may be used to guide an aircraft to an initial submarine search area?
7. What are the features of a basic, air-launched sonobuoy?

8. What are the steps in any hunt for a submarine from its detection through to a kill?
9. List four means of detecting a submarine without using acoustics.

Chapter 3   Anti-Submarine Warfare Aircraft
1. List the requirements for an effective land-based, fixed-wing, anti-submarine warfare aircraft.
2. What is the principle behind the employment of a magnetic anomaly detector?
3. Describe one active and one passive sonobuoy.
4. Describe the *Stingray* torpedo.
5. What is significant about the composition of the staff controlling the NATO Eastern Atlantic anti-submarine warfare aircraft?
6. Describe the advantages of land-based, fixed-wing aircraft in anti-submarine warfare.

Chapter 4   Anti-Surface Unit Warfare
1. Define anti-surface unit warfare.
2. What are the factors affecting anti-surface unit warfare?
3. List the advantages of land-based, fixed-wing aircraft in the anti-surface unit warfare role.
4. Describe some of the defences employed by ships against attacking aircraft.
5. Describe the Soviet battle-cruiser, *Kirov*.

Chapter 5   Anti-Ship Aircraft
1. Describe the *Sea Eagle* missile.
2. Describe a typical sortie profile by the *Buccaneer* anti-ship aircraft.
3. What are the advantages of the US Air Force B52 in the anti-shipping role?
4. What is third-party targeting in anti-ship attacks?
5. What was the principal lesson learnt from the *Exocet* attack against USS *Stark* in May 1987 in the Gulf?
6. What is the fundamental difference between Western and Soviet anti-ship missiles?

Chapter 6   Maritime Air Defence
1. Describe some methods a surface force may use to achieve deception and concealment at sea.
2. Describe the layers in a complete air-defence system.
3. List the advantages of land-based AEW aircraft over their carrier-borne equivalents.
4. Describe the ways of defending a large AEW aircraft.
5. How may a fighter extend its time on CAP?
6. What is the advantage to Britain of operating fighters on CAPS to defend a surface force in the north Norwegian Sea?
7. In the Falklands Campaign how did the Royal Navy attempt to overcome the lack of effective AEW cover?

Chapter 7   Air–Sea Rescue
1. Define the phrase 'search and rescue'.
2. Describe the two Search and Rescue Regions for which Britain is responsible and name the location of the Rescue Co-ordination Centre for each Region.
3. As well as the two SRRs in Britain, where else might the RAF also provide a Search and Rescue Service?
4. List the resources available for search and rescue within Britain.
5. List four of the factors which will determine the conduct of the search.
6. Describe three of the types of search likely to be used.
7. What is the primary role of the on-scene commander in a search and rescue incident?

Chapter 8   Looking Ahead
1. Explain the terms 'whole concept approach' and 'replacement approach' when considering new defence equipment.
2. List the advantages and disadvantages of using a large common airframe in various roles.
3. Explain three non-acoustic methods of detecting submerged submarines.
4. Describe the advantages to be gained by penetrating ice with a sonobuoy; list the features required in a cost-effective, air-delivered system for ice penetration.
5. Is a NATO maritime patrol force a viable proposition?
6. How might cost effectiveness be achieved in maintaining a fast jet maritime strike/attack capability?

Bibliography

BOOKS

Air Defence, M.B. Elsam (Brassey's). London 1989.
Aircraft versus Submarine, Alfred Price (Jane's). London 1980.
Coastal Command at War, T. Dudley-Gordon (Jarrolds). London 1943.
Seek and Strike, W. Hackmann (HMSO). London 1984.
Anti-Submarine Warfare, J.R. Hill (Ian Allan). Shepperton 1984.
Air Defence at Sea, J.R. Hill (Ian Allan). Shepperton 1987.
The Ships and Aircraft of the US fleet, N. Polmar (Arms & Armour Press). London
    1987.
An Illustrated Guide to Modern Naval Aviation and Aircraft Carriers, J. Jordan
    (Salamander). London 1983.
BAe Nimrod, J. Chartres (Ian Allan). Shepperton 1986.
Jane's Naval Review, J. Moore [ed.] (Jane's). London 1987.
Per Ardua ad Astra, M. Donne & C. Fowler (Muller). London 1982.
Thorn EMI: 50 Years of Radar, D. Martin (Thorn EMI Electronics).
Helicopter Rescue, J. Chartres (Ian Allan). Shepperton 1950.
The Royal Air Force Today and Tomorrow, R.E. Mason (Ian Allan). Shepperton
    1982.
The RAF in Action, R. Jackson (Blandford). Poole 1985.
Modern Submarine Warfare, D. Miller & J. Jordan (Salamander). London 1987.
Jane's All the World's Aircraft, J.W.R. Taylor [ed.] (Jane's). Annual.
Jane's Fighting Ships, R. Sharpe [ed.] (Jane's). Annual.
Jane's Air-Launched Weapons, D. Lennox [ed.] (Jane's). London 1990.
Right of the Line, J. Terraine (Hodder & Stoughton). London 1985.
The U-Boat War in the Atlantic 1939–1945, G. Hessler (HMSO). London 1989.
Flight Test Techniques for Nimrod, AGARD Conference Proceedings No. 373,
    Neuilly Sur Seine 1984.

PERIODICAL ARTICLES AND BOOK EXTRACTS

'NATO's navies on the move', NATO'S sixteen Nations, September 1989. Vol 34, No 5.

'Over the horizon detection and targeting in the Soviet Navy', M. Vego, *Jane's Soviet Intelligence Review*, July 1989.

'Non-acoustic ASW looks to the 21st century', S. Elliott, *Jane's Defence Weekly*, 1 July 1989.

'Soviet advances in underwater detection systems', R. Corlett, *Maritime*.

'The air threat against ships', A. Preston, *Asian Defence Journal*, 6/1989.

'Sonobuoys and dipping sonars', M. Hewish, *International Defense Review*, 6/1989.

'Ice-penetrating sonobuoy system breaks the high Arctic barrier', J.R. Bavvette & J. Courtenay Lewis *Sea Technology*, October 1988.

'Stealth submarines versus ASW', *National Defence*, March 1989.

'Scientific and technological problems in undersea warfare', R. Benjamin, *JRNSS*, vol 23, no. 1.

'Stalking the silent—emerging challenges in ASW', J.E. Moore. *Defense & Foreign Affairs*, September 1987.

'The non-acoustic detection of submarines', T. Stefanick, *Scientific American*, March 1988.

'Maritime patrol aircraft', B. Walters, *Defence*, January 1984.

'The Penguin Mk 3 air-launched anti-ship missile', *International Defense Review*, 1/1983.

'The influence of shore-based aircraft on naval strategy', T. Wilt, *Naval Forces*, 1/1984.

'The deadly Harpoon', A. Preston, *Defence*, May 1981.

'Anti-ship missiles—the sea-skimming threat', B. Wanstall, *Interavia*, 10/1984.

'Naval Air Wing 1 of the Federal German Navy', *Navy International*, March 1984.

'Soviet maritime air power', P. Beaver, *Navy International*, December 1982.

'Maritime surveillance aircraft—a growth market', R. Salvy, *Armada International*, January/February 1982.

'Exocet—the world's first sea skimmer', A Preston, *Warship* No. 24, 1982.

'How invisible is the Exocet missile?', C. Heath, *Pacific Defence Reporter*, July 1982.

'Real-time ocean surveillance', N. Friedman, *Military Technology*, 9/1984.

'Soviet Navy ASW aviation', M. Vego, *Navy International*, June 1984.

'ASW systems for aircraft', *Navy International*, September 1984.

'Defending against anti-ship missiles', A. Preston, *Defence*, August 1989.

'Kormoran 2', *Interavia*, 9/1985.

'Anti-ship missile: Sea Eagle', E. Hooton, *NATO's Sixteen Nations*, September/October 1984.

'The north Atlantic's listening force', J.J. Lok, *Jane's Defence Weekly*, October 1989.

'Standing NATO MPA force proposed', J.J. Lok, *Jane's Defence Weekly*.

'Naval air power', A. Preston, *Asian Defence Journal*, 10/89.

'Anti-submarine warfare: the state of the art', J. Jordan, *Modern Navy—Seascape*, December 1987.

'Sonar—seeing more clearly now', B. Blake, *Jane's Naval Review 1987*.

'An ear to the sea', D. Charles, *New Scientist*, 14 October 1989.

'Guardians of the oceans', M.J. Gething, *Defence*, July 1989.

'After Orion', J. Bailey, *Flight International*, 2 September 1989.

'ASW operations with Patwing II', T. Nash, *Armed Forces*, May 1989.

'ASW requirements for the Third World', *Naval Forces*, 1/1989.

'Defeating the submarine: choosing ASW strategies,' J.S. Breemer, *Naval Forces*, IV/1989.

'Quiet Soviet submarines pose new threat', D.Wettern, *Pacific Defence Reporter*, October 1989.

'Anti-submarine warfare—sonics, sensors and systems', M. Witt, *Asian Defence Journal*, 6/1989.

'Anti-submarine warfare—the role of airborne forces', B. Walters, *Navy International*, July/August 1988.

'Maintaining the edge in US ASW', R. O'Rourke, *Navy International*, July/August 1988.

'Joint operations in ASW', M. Vego, *Navy International*, May 1985.

'A survey of Western ASW in 1985', N. Friedman, *International Defense Review*, 10/1985.

'The Sea Eagle anti-ship missile', M. Hewish. *International Defense Review*, 7/1984.

'Submarine hunter', J.S. Porth, *Defense & Foreign Affairs*, July 1982.

'ASW systems for aircraft', *Navy International*, October 1984.

'Maritime air power', *Air Clues*, March 1984.

'The impact of future surface ships and aircraft on anti-submarine warfare', M.C. Eames, *Canadian Defense Quarterly*, December 1989.

'ASW weapons and tactics', J.R. Hill, *Naval Forces*, VI/1989.

'Maritime patrol radars for the 1990s', D. Crabtree, Thorn EMI Electronics.

'Soviet sonar technology', J. Bussert. *Jane's Soviet Intelligence Review*, October 1989.

'ASW sensors', M. Hewish, *International Defense Review*, 8/1987.

'Soviet maritime strategy', D. Conley, *US Naval Institute Proceedings*, September 1989.

'The future of NATO's forward maritime strategy', T.J.H. Laurence, *RUSI/Brassey's Defence Yearbook 1990*.

'Maritime airpower after 2000', Air Marshal Sir B. Duxbury, paper to conference on the future of British air power, King's College London, July 1987.

'Future challenges for British defence policy', Marshal of the RAF Sir D. Craig, *RUSI/Brassey's Defence Yearbook 1990*.

'Air defence of merchant ships', J.A. Boutilier, *Journal of the Australian Naval Institute*, August 1989.

'Harpoon employment in naval anti-submarine warfare', Grosick, Massey & Petersen, US Air Force Air War College Research Report, 1988.

Index